Fauna of
New Zealand
Ko te Aitanga Pepeke
o Aotearoa

Fauna of New Zealand
Ko te Aitanga Pepeke o Aotearoa
Number / Nama 33

Moranilini
(Insecta: Hymenoptera)

J. A. Berry

Manaaki Whenua - Landcare Research
Biodiversity and Conservation Group
Mount Albert Research Centre
Private Bag 92170, Auckland
New Zealand

Manaaki
Whenua
PRESS

Lincoln, Canterbury, New Zealand
1995

Cataloguing in publication

BERRY, Jocelyn Asha
    Moranilini (Insecta: Hymenoptera) / J.A. Berry. – Lincoln,
Canterbury, New Zealand, Manaaki Whenua Press, 1995.
    (Fauna of New Zealand, ISSN 0111–5383 ; no. 33).
    ISBN 0-478-04538-7

    I. Title   II. Series

    UDC 595.79(931)

Prepared for publication by the Series Editor using computer-based text processing, layout, and printing at Landcare Research New Zealand Ltd, Mt Albert Research Centre, Private Bag 92170, Auckland, N.Z.

Maori text by UniServices Translation Centre, Auckland

Printed by GP Print Ltd, Wellington

Published by Manaaki Whenua Press, Landcare Research New Zealand Ltd,
P.O. Box 40, Lincoln, Canterbury, New Zealand

Front cover: The insect depicted is *Aphobetus paucisetosus*, female
Aro mua: Ko te kararehe nei ko *Aphobetus paucisetosus*, hine

Class / Karaaihe **Insecta**

Order / Oota **Hymenoptera**

Superfamily / Whaamere-nui **Chalcidoidea**

Family / Whaamere **Pteromalidae**

Subfamily / Whaamere-iti **Eunotinae**

Tribe / Hapu **Moranilini**

Moraniline wasps

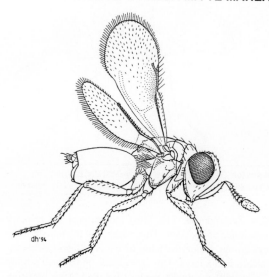

dh'94

Illustration: *Moranila strigaster*, female (Illustrator: D.W. Helmore)
Whakaahua: *Moranila strigaster*, hine (Kai-whakaahua: D.W. Helmore)

The moraniline wasps are a small group, both in number of species (64 described worldwide) and in their individual size: at 1–3 mm in length they are little bigger than a large pinhead. They are rather distinctive within the larger group of mostly parasitic wasps known as the chalcidoids. Even though most species are fully winged, one-third of the endemic New Zealand species have reduced wings.

Owing to their abundance and diversity, and the problems inherent in studying such minute insects, the chalcidoid fauna of New Zealand is poorly known. Until recently only five species of Moranilini had been recorded from New Zealand. Now seventeen species in three genera are recognised, of which eleven are found nowhere else and are assumed to be endemic. The other six species are found also in Australia.

Despite their small size and relative scarcity, moraniline wasps are interesting because of their life history and their restricted distribution. They occur naturally only in the region between New Zealand and India, with the greatest number and diversity of species in Australia. It is likely that the Moranilini were derived in Australia from chalcidoid ancestral stock, and that their diversity in this part of the world is due to their evolution in isolation here.

With a few exceptions the moraniline wasps are natural enemies of Coccoidea, a group including scale insects, mealybugs or pseudococcids (see 'Fauna of New Zealand' no. 11), and giant mealybugs or margarodids (see 'Fauna of

(continued overleaf)

He roopu iti noa iho te katipoo o hapuu Moranilini onaa hua oona momo (he ono tekau maa whaa anoo kua tauiratia i te ao katoa), aa, i te nuinga o te mea kotahi: kotahi ki te toru mira mita (mm) te roa, heoi waahi nui atu i te upoko pine nui. Ka kitea tonu raatou i waenga i nga katipoo roopu nui haamana taapiri e kiia nei he Chalcidoidea. Ahakoa nei na ko te nuinga o taua momo ka whaanui nga parirau, kotahi torunga o nga katipoo tuuturu no konei anoo no Niu Tiireni Aotearoa nei, e whai parirau nonohi ana.

Na te mea i te kaha tini me nga aahua momo katoa, aa, me nga aahua momo i raruraru mai raano i te tauira i eenei ngaarara iti, kaahore i moohio rawatia te aahua o te whaamere-nui Chalcidoidea i Niu Tiireni Aotearoa nei. I mua tata atu e rima anoo nga momo o hapuu Moranilini kua rekoatahia i Niu Tiireni Aotearoa. Inaianinei tekau maa whitu momo heke iho mai i nga taatai e toru ko moohiotia, tekau maa tahi e kore kitea i hea atu, e whakapaingia ana he tuuturu no konei tonu. Ko nga toenga momo he ono, ka kitea ono i Ahitereiria.

Ahakoa he iti noa iho me te tata kore e kitea, kanui anoo te hiitoria aahua noho ora, aa, me te iti hoki o nga waahi ka kitea ai raatou. Heoi, ka puta mai i nga takiwaa i waenga i i Niu Tiireni me Iinia, araa, te nuinga me nga aahua momoka kitea i Ahitereiria ko te whakaaro i puutake mai anoo a whaamere-nui Chalcidoidea i nga tuupuna i Ahitereiria, aa, me nga aahua momo katoa i teenei waahi o te ao i haangai mai anoo i too raatou tupuranga raatou anahe i konei.

Ko te nuinga ehara ko te katoa, ko te hapuu katipoo Moranilini mai ra anoo he hoa riri, no te roopu nei, kei roto

(ara haere tonu)

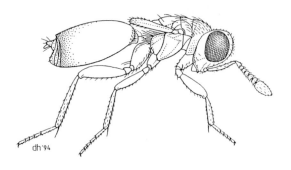

Illustration: *Ophelosia mcglashani*, female (Illustrator: D.W. Helmore)
Whakaahua: *Ophelosia mcglashani*, hine (Kai-whakaahua: D.W. Helmore)

New Zealand' no. 21). Most moranilines are primary parasitoids of coccoids. This means that the female wasp lays an egg inside the body of the host insect, where it hatches into a larva. This larva feeds on the host's body tissues until eventually the host is killed. After pupating inside the empty skin of the host, a new adult wasp emerges. (Note that a parasitoid kills its host, whereas a parasite usually does not.)

A few moranilines are predators, living in the woolly egg-sacs produced by female mealybugs and feeding on her eggs. These species pupate inside the egg-sacs, emerging as adults which seek out further mealybugs in which to continue the life cycle.

A very small number of moraniline species act as hyperparasitoids, developing inside the body of a parasitoid of another species which is itself developing inside the host insect.

The host insects are plant sap feeders, and some introduced species—particularly of mealybugs—can become pests in horticultural situations. They are hard to control with insecticides, because the adult females cover themselves in waxy secretions, and tend to occupy sheltered places on their host plants. Natural enemies such as moraniline wasps can be used as biological control agents, to reduce their numbers.

Contributor Jocelyn Berry was born in India. She completed an MSc in zoology at The University of Auckland in 1983, and has recently graduated from the Australian National University, Canberra, with a PhD thesis on the systematics of the Australasian Eunotinae. In 1983 she was employed by the Entomology Division of DSIR, and is currently a scientist with the Biodiversity and Conservation Group of Manaaki Whenua - Landcare Research specialising in Hymenoptera. Jo has had a special interest in biological control since her undergraduate days.

anoo nei nga ngaarara 'mealybugs,' me nga Pseudococcidae (tirohia *Fauna of New Zealand / Ko te Aitanga Pepeke o Aotearoa* nama 11), me nga ngaarara mealybug he tupua, he Margarodidae raanei (tirohia *Fauna of New Zealand / Ko te Aitanga Pepeke o Aotearoa* nama 21). Ko te nuinga o hapuu Moranilini he momonui i te haamana taapiri kaikai 'parasitoids,' kaikai i teena mea i te ngaarara momo Coccoidea. Ko teenei tikanga ka paa ki te katipoo uwha, ka whakawhaanau i tana heeki ki roto i te tinana ngaarara ora. I reira ka peehi ka puta mai ko te keto. Ko te keto ka kaikai mai maa roto mai i nga wheekau ngaarara, aa, mate noa te ngaarara. I muri i te moe roa i roto i te kiri kaahore nei he mea i roto, ka puta mai he katipoo hoou (kia mahara, ko te momo nei a parasitoid, ka huri kaikai i te ngaarara ka nohoina nei e ia aa mate noa, haaunga anoo te momo haamana taapiri e kore peenei).

Ko eetahi o hapuu Moranilini he kaipatupatu. Ka noho i roto i nga peeke wuuru e haanga mai ana e nga uwha mealybugs, ka tahuri kaikai i oonaa heeki. Ko teenei momo ka tupu i roto i nga peeke wuuru, ka puta mai he pakeke i te whaiwhai haere anoo i nga ngaarara mealybugs kia haere hirirauna tonu ai te wiira ora.

Takitahi noa iho nga momo ka peenei i te 'hyperparasitoids' nei ka aata tupu haere i roto i te tinana o teetahi atu parasitoid e tupu haere ana anoo i roto i te tinana ngaarara.

Ko nga ngaarara e kainga ana, he ngaarara kai wai raakau, aa, eetahi ngaarara mealybug hoki i uru noa mai — ka huri whakahoohaa whakaruraru i roto i nga mahi ahuwhenua. Kanui anoo te pakeke ki te whakaiti ki nga paihana ngaarara, no te mea ko nga uwha ka tuku wai pakeke hei whakakahu tinana hei aarai ia raatou, araa, ka noho hoki ka kuhu i nga waahi ruruhau o nga raakau (e kaia nei e raatou). Ko nga hoa riri tuuturu peenei ia katipoo Moranilini nei, ka taaea i te tuku atu hei kai whiu hei toa whakaiti, ngaarara, hei aawhina taiao.

*Ko te kaituhi ko **Jocelyn Berry** i whaanau mai i Iinia. Ka mutu tana tohu maatauranga MSc i Zoology i te Whare Waananga o Aakarana i te tau 1983, aa, i muri atu ka puta mai i te Whaare Waananga Nahirana o Ahitereiria, i te rohe o Canberra me te tohu taakuta PhD. Ko tana tuhi rangahau e paa ana ki te aahuatanga o te Eunotinae ki nga takiwaa katoa o Ahitereiria. I te tau 1983 ka mahi i te wehenga rangahau ngaarara Entomology o DSIR. Inaininei ka mahi puutaiao ia i nga waahanga roopu Biodiversity Tiaki Taiao o Manaaki Whenua - Landcare Research, ko tana tino mahi tohungatanga ko Hymenoptera. Mai anoo i nga raa ia ia e tauira ana e ako tonu ana hoki mo ana tohu, ko te tino mea nui anoo kia Jo ko te mahi titiro momo ngaarara whakaiti ngaarara, hei kai aawhina hoki mo te tai ao.*

ABSTRACT

The tribe Moranilini has an Australasian (particularly Australian) distribution, and its members are mostly parasitoids and egg predators of coccoids (Hemiptera). Three genera are recognised in New Zealand – *Aphobetus* Howard, *Moranila* Cameron, and *Ophelosia* Riley. *Modronila* Bouček and *Pidinka* Bouček are regarded as junior synonyms of *Aphobetus*. Nine new species are described: *Aphobetus cultratus*, *A. erroli*, *A. paucisetosus*, *Moranila aotearoae*, *M. strigaster*, *Ophelosia australis*, *O. charlesi*, *O. mcglashani*, and *O. stenopteryx*. Eight species are redescribed: *Aphobetus cyanea* (Bouček), *A. maskelli* Howard, *A. nana* (Bouček), *Moranila californica* (Howard), *M. comperei* (Ashmead), *Ophelosia bifasciata* Girault, *O. crawfordi* Riley, and *O. keatsi* Girault. Seven synonymies are proposed: *Moranila comperei* = *Tomocera saissetiae* Girault, *T. transversifasciata* Girault, and *T. io* Girault; *Ophelosia bifasciata* = *O. viridinotata* Girault; *O. crawfordi* = *O. sulcata* Girault; *O. keatsi* = *O. horatii* Girault. Lectotypes are designated for *Aphobetus maskelli*, *Tomocera transversifasciata*, and *Ophelosia sulcata*.

Keys to the genera and species of Moranilini found in New Zealand are presented. Host relationships are examined, and possible areas of origin of widely distributed species are discussed. Evidence from host relationships, biogeographic events, and phylogeny suggest that the Moranilini originated in Australia, and that a minimum of five dispersal events to New Zealand have occurred. A vicariance argument to account for the biogeography of the tribe would require some lineages of at least 80 million years duration; this is considered unlikely. It is not known whether the tribe Moranilini occurs in South America, but if it does then this would suggest a minimum age for the tribe of around 55 million years.

The biological control of *Pseudococcus longispinus* (Targioni-Tozzetti), *P. calceolariae* Maskell, and *P. affinis* (Maskell) in New Zealand is discussed. Two of these, and possibly the third, are of Australian origin. From host relationship and distribution data it is concluded that all known natural enemies in the Moranilini are well established here.

A checklist of taxa, a host/parasitoid list, and species distribution maps are included.

CHECKLIST OF TAXA

CONTENTS

ACKNOWLEDGMENTS

This study was made possible by a DSIR scholarship, which enabled me to spend three years at the Australian National Insect Collection, CSIRO, Canberra. I am grateful to Max Whitten, Ebbe Nielsen, and Ian Naumann (CSIRO) and to John Longworth and John Dugdale (Landcare Research) for making this stay possible.

I am also grateful to the following people: Helen Geier and Mark Dominick (CSIRO) took the electron micrographs; Mark Dominick developed the prints, and Colin Beaton (CSIRO) provided advice; John LaSalle (IIEL) provided specimens; Gordon Nishida (BPBM) helped with access to specimens in Honolulu; Eric Grissell (U.S. Department of Agriculture) provided specimens and advice; Andy Austin and Paul Dangerfield provided specimens from the Waite Institute; the late Gudrun Sarnes (QMBA) and Jan Forrest (SAMA) helped locate Girault types.

Veronica Brancatini and Jamie Seymour (CSIRO, Indooroopilly) provided hosts and specimens from Queensland. James Altmann (Biological Services, Loxton) provided hosts and specimens from South Australia. Errol Valentine (DSIR) contributed much of the reared material to the NZAC. John Charles (HortResearch) collected and reared many specimens of *Ophelosia* from New Zealand.

Ken Key (CSIRO) provided advice on etymology. Mary Carver (CSIRO) and Penny Gullan (Australian National University) helped to find host families. Mary Carver provided insight on parasitoid/host relationships and information on host records for *Moranila* and *Ophelosia*. Ian Naumann (CSIRO) sorted much of the ANIC material to species. Josephine Cardale (CSIRO) helped with curatorial matters. Rosa Henderson (Landcare Research) looked up map co-ordinates for distributions of New Zealand species.

Gordon Gordh (University of Queensland), Eric Grissell, Andy Austin, Ian Naumann, and (particularly) Penny Gullan made many helpful comments on the original text, and John Dugdale (Landcare Research) and John Charles (HortResearch) commented on sections. Ricardo Palma (MONZ) made useful comments on the final draft.

Lastly, I would like to thank Dr Beverley Holloway for support during her time as leader of the Systematics Group of Entomology Division, DSIR.

INTRODUCTION

The higher classification of the group of microhymenoptera known as chalcidoids has a confused history. Use of the name Chalcidoidea dates from Ashmead (1899), who upgraded the family Chalcididae to superfamily rank, recognising 14 constituent families. Since that time the number of families recognised has ranged from one (Handlirsch 1925) to 24 (Nikol'skaya 1952). At present 21 families are generally accepted as valid (Bouček 1988a).

The family Pteromalidae is one of the largest in the Chalcidoidea, consisting of about 3000 (2800: Grissell & Schauff 1990; 3100: Gauld & Bolton 1988) morphologically and biologically diverse species. Although the pteromalids have always been recognised as a discrete group within the chalcidoids, their history is far from straightforward. Family composition varies from author to author, and now includes many subfamilies which were formerly ranked as separate families, e.g., Cleonyminae, Spalangiinae, Miscogasterinae, Ormocerinae, Pireninae, and Sphegigasterinae (Bouček 1988b). Other groups currently accorded family rank have at times been included as subfamilies in the Pteromalidae, e.g., Perilampidae, Eucharitidae, and Ormyridae. Grissell & Schauff (1990) regard the Pteromalidae as the most artificial grouping within the Chalcidoidea, and according to Heraty & Darling (1984) the family is a repository for monophyletic groups not readily placed elsewhere and not considered to warrant separate family status. The family Pteromalidae undoubtedly includes many highly specialised smaller groups, which makes it almost impossible to define the features held in common. Bouček (1988b) cites examples of character states diagnostic of most pteromalids, but recognises that there are no universally diagnostic features. Some subfamilies stand out as being particularly apomorphic, but can be recognised as being related to successively less derived groups (detailed in Bouček 1988b).

The eunotines were first mentioned as a group by Walker (1872), who called them a "small, distinct family." They were formally called the subfamily Eunotinae by Ashmead (1904), who included the genera *Anysis* Howard, *Cardiogaster* Motschulsky, *Cephaleta* Motschulsky, *Euargopelte* Förster, *Eurycranium* Ashmead, *Eunotus* Walker, *Mnoonema* Motschulsky, *Muscidea* Motschulsky, *Scutellista* Motschulsky, and *Solenoderus* Motschulsky. Of these only *Scutellista* and *Cephaleta* occur in Australasia (both probably introduced from the Oriental region), and none have been recorded from New Zealand.

Diagnosis of the Eunotinae

The most recent definition of the group (Bouček 1988a) lists the following character states, the combination of which diagnoses the subfamily Eunotinae:
- head and genae carinate;
- male antennae with 4 funicular segments;
- female antennae usually with 5 funicular segments;
- notauli always complete;
- thorax usually with paired setae;
- 1st gastral tergite usually at least half length of gaster.

In his revision Bouček erected three tribes of Eunotinae:

EUNOTINI – characterised by regular, short pilosity over the entire scutellum and by the posterior of the scutellum being produced over the propodeum. Five genera, all from the Northern Hemisphere, but two with secondarily Australasian distributions.

TOMOCERODINI – characterised by the scutellar pilosity being restricted to two pairs of setae (usually), and the second gastral tergite being longer than the first. One genus of two species (one undescribed), which occurs only in Mexico and Arizona.

MORANILINI – characterised by the first gastral tergite being the longest, usually covering more than half the gaster. Sixteen genera, almost exclusively southern in distribution.

The tribes Eunotini and Tomocerodini are thus Northern Hemisphere (Nearctic) in distribution, and the Moranilini are almost exclusively southern (Oriental and Australian).

Of the 16 moraniline genera included in Bouček's 1988a revision, only two were relatively speciose: *Ophelosia* Riley (15 species) and *Moranila* Cameron (10 species). *Aphobetus* Howard had four species and *Tomicobomorpha* Girault two species. The remaining 12 genera were monotypic. Such a high level of monotypy suggests (a) that many species in these genera have yet to be collected, and/or (b) that the generic concept used is not correct, i.e., the monotypic genera may be derived members of larger genera, having been separated on the basis of one or two autapomorphies, but which more properly belong in larger genera.

BIOLOGY OF THE MORANILINI

In general, Moranilini are associated with Sternorrhyncha (Hemiptera), mostly as parasitoids or egg predators of Coccoidea ('scale insects,' including mealybugs or pseudococcids and margarodids). They are occasionally associated with Aleyrodidae (whiteflies) or Aphididae. Since these groups of Hemiptera are often pests of economic importance, their natural enemies are of interest as biological control agents.

Host relationships

All known host relationships of Moranilini found in New Zealand are discussed here. Host records from New Zealand can be found under the 'Biology' section in the species descriptions or in the Appendix, where authorship of host names is given and systematic affiliations are specified.

Aphobetus. Species of *Aphobetus* are parasitoids or hyperparasitoids of Coccoidea or Aphididae. Even when numerous, rearing records show little host specificity.

A. cyanea is a primary parasitoid of Eriococcidae. It has been reared from an unidentified species of *Eriococcus* on *Danthonia* and *Chionochloa* (both native tussock grasses); and from *Eriococcus nitidulus*, endemic to New Zealand (Hoy 1962), on *Poa caespitosa* (native tussock grass). *A. cyanea* has an alpine distribution (Map 2), being restricted to habitats in which the native tussock grows.

A. maskelli has been reared from *Nipaecoccus aurilanatus*; an unidentified species of *Leucaspis*; *Ctenochiton viridis*, an endemic New Zealand species (Ben-Dov 1993); *Inglisia leptospermi*, also an endemic New Zealand species (Ben-Dov 1993); and *Powellia* sp.

A. nana has been reared from the coccids *Ctenochiton viridis*, *C. perforatus*, an endemic New Zealand species (Ben-Dov 1993); *C. piperis*, found in New Zealand and the Pacific region (Ben-Dov 1993); *C. elaeocarpi*, an endemic New Zealand species (Ben-Dov 1993); *Pseudococcus longispinus*; and *Leucaspis mixta*.

A. paucisetosus has been reared from an unidentified species of *Leucaspis*; and from several native species of Eriococcidae.

An Australian species has been reared from an unidentified species of *Eriococcus*.

Moranila. *Moranila* species do not appear to be host-specific; where a number of records are available, a range of families is parasitised.

M. californica has been reared from the following hosts. ASTEROLECANIDAE. *Asterolecanium pustulans*, a common species found throughout the tropics and sometimes occurring in temperate areas (Williams & Watson 1990), but not found in Australia or New Zealand (Commonwealth Institute of Entomology 1984).

COCCIDAE. *Saissetia oleae*, which is cosmopolitan but is probably of South African origin (Delucchi *et al.* 1976). According to Morales (1989, p. 237) *S. oleae* occurs in both Australia and New Zealand, although Ben-Dov (1993) does not list it as occurring in either country. *Parasaissetia* (=*Saissettia*) *nigra*, cosmopolitan including Australia, New Zealand, and P.N.G. (Ben-Dov 1993). *S. coffeae* (=*S. hemisphaerica*), a very common tropicopolitan species (Williams & Watson 1990), introduced to Australia (Williams 1991). Ben-Dov (1993) lists *S. coffeae* as present in New Zealand, but Williams & Watson (1990) do not. *Ceroplastes sinensis*, cosmopolitan (including New Zealand and Australia), but probably of South American origin (Qin *et al.*, in press). *C. rubens*, tropicopolitan and temperate (Williams & Watson 1990), occurring in Australia and parts of the Pacific but not in New Zealand (Ben-Dov 1993). *C. rusci*, temperate (Williams & Watson 1990), not present in Australia or New Zealand (Ben-Dov 1993). *C. ceriferus*, Southeast Asia, Australia, Papua New Guinea, parts of the Pacific, and introduced into the U.S. (Williams & Watson 1990), but not present in New Zealand (Ben-Dov 1993). *Coccus hesperidum*, cosmopolitan (Williams & Watson 1990), introduced into Australia (Williams 1991) and New Zealand (Ben-Dov 1993).

PSEUDOCOCCIDAE. *Chaetococcus* (=*Antonina*) *bambusae*, found in Australia (Williams 1985) but not present in New Zealand (Cox 1987).

M. comperei has been reared from *Saissetia oleae*; as a primary parasitoid of *Nipaecoccus aurilanatus*; as a hyperparasite of Aphididae through Braconidae; is a probable hyperparasitoid of Aleyrodidae through Mymaridae; and has been reared in unknown circumstances from Psyllidae.

Two Australian species have been reared from unidentified species of *Eriococcus*.

Ophelosia. Species of *Ophelosia* fall into two groups. (i) Margarodid egg predators (host range narrow). *O. crawfordi* has only been recorded feeding on the eggs of two species of *Icerya*: *I. purchasi*, which is cosmopolitan but is thought to have originated in Australia (Williams & Watson 1990), and *I. seychellarum*, which is present in Australia and has been intercepted in New Zealand but has not established (Morales 1991). *O. crawfordi* has spread to other parts of the world with the movement of its hosts. An Australian species, *O. hypatia*, is host-specific to *I. purchasi* eggs.

(ii) Pseudococcid exploiters (host range wide). *O. bifasciata* has been reared from: *Pseudococcus calceolariae*, which is found in both Australia and New Zealand but which is of Australian origin according to Cox (1987) and Williams (1985); *Pseudococcus longispinus*, which is cosmopolitan, though Williams (1985) presents evidence that it is Australian in origin. *P. longispinus* was first recorded

in New Zealand in 1890 (Cox 1987); *Planococcus citri*, which Williams (1985) also considers to be Australian in origin, but which is also found in the Pacific (Williams 1985) but not in New Zealand (Cox 1987); *Pseudoripersia turgipes*, Australian (Williams 1985) and not found in New Zealand (Cox 1987); *Nipaecoccus aurilanatus*, introduced to New Zealand from Australia, and present in the U.S. (Cox 1987).

O. charlesi is almost exclusively a predator of pseudococcid ovisacs. Its host species are *Paraferrisia podocarpi*, endemic to New Zealand (Cox 1987); *Pseudococcus affinis*, found in Australia and New Zealand but North American in origin according to Cox (1987), though Williams (1985, p. 9) considers it to be Australian; *Phenacoccus graminicola*, also found in New Zealand but North American in origin (Cox 1987); *P. longispinus*; and *P. calceolariae*.

O. keatsi has been reared from *P. longispinus*, *P. affinis*, and *Phenacoccus graminicola*.

An Indian species has been recorded from an unidentified species of *Nipaecoccus*, and from *Planococcus citri*.

BIOGEOGRAPHY OF THE EUNOTINAE

Current distribution

Representatives of the subfamily Eunotinae are found worldwide. When the subfamily is broken into tribes, however, the distributions are seen to be clearly disjunct. The Eunotini and Tomocerodini have a Northern Hemisphere distribution, while the Moranilini occur almost exclusively in the Southern Hemisphere. A summary of the distribution of the genera occurring in New Zealand follows.

Aphobetus occurs in Australia and New Zealand, but there is no overlap of species. Six species are endemic to New Zealand, and the remaining eight to Australia.

Moranila californica is cosmopolitan. *M. comperei* is distributed throughout Australia, and has recently been collected in New Zealand. Eleven further *Moranila* species are endemic to Australia, and two are endemic to New Zealand.

Ophelosia has been recorded from North America, India, Papua New Guinea, Java, Australia, and New Zealand. This distribution suggests that it occurs throughout Asia, but has not been more widely collected. *O. bifasciata* is distributed throughout mainland Australia, New Zealand, and Papua New Guinea. *O. charlesi* is found in eastern Australia and New Zealand. Eight further species are endemic to Australia; two species appear to be endemic to Papua New Guinea (but are represented by only one specimen each); one species has been collected only in

India; and two brachypterous and one narrow-winged species are endemic to New Zealand. *O. crawfordi* occurs in North America, Java, eastern Australia, and New Zealand. *O. keatsi* occurs in Australia and New Zealand.

Endemism in the Moranilini

A consensus cladogram of the 309 minimum-length trees produced by an analysis of the world species of the Moranilini (Berry 1994) is presented as Text-fig. 1. Some relationships will be alluded to in the following sections.

Seventeen species of Moranilini have been recorded from New Zealand. Of these, all six species of *Aphobetus*, three of *Ophelosia*, and two of *Moranila* have not been recorded from anywhere else, and are assumed to be endemic. Thus 11 of 17 species in the tribe, or 65%, are endemic to New Zealand. There are no endemic genera. The remaining six species have been recorded from other places, and thus their area of origin is uncertain. Each is discussed below, and an attempt is made to assign endemism on the basis of the available evidence.

Moranila californica has the widest distribution of any member of the tribe, having been collected from all biogeographical regions. It also has the widest host range for the tribe, having been recorded occasionally as a hyperparasitoid or egg predator, but most commonly as a primary parasitoid of Asterolecaniidae, Pseudococcidae, and Coccidae, particularly *Saissetia* and *Ceroplastes*. Many of the hosts are also cosmopolitan in distribution and cannot be used to help determine the origin of *M. californica*. In the consensus tree (Text-fig. 1) the *Moranila* group was largely unresolved, but *M. californica* is most closely related to *Moranila viridivertex* and *M.* 'n. sp. 1' (Berry, in prep.), both Australian species. This indicates a possible Australian origin for *M. californica*, with its propensity for host-switching allowing a wide distribution.

Moranila comperei is recorded from Australia and, very rarely, New Zealand. Its hosts include one Australian species, and the cladogram (Text-fig. 1) indicates that it is most closely related to an Australian species, *M.* 'n. sp. 3.'

Ophelosia bifasciata is recorded from Papua New Guinea, mainland Australia, and the North Island of New Zealand. The recorded hosts are all Australian. Although this species is commonly collected in New Zealand, the earliest date of collection is 1966. The known distribution (Map 12) shows that *O. bifasciata* has been collected from the major citrus-growing regions in the North Island, tracking its hosts. I concluded that *O. bifasciata* is Australian in origin, and has been introduced into New Zealand along with its hosts.

The hosts of *O. charlesi* are not indicative of its origin. *Pseudococcus longispinus* and *P. calceolariae* are Australian, *P. affinis* and *Phenacoccus graminicola* are possibly

Table 1 Levels of endemism of Moranilini in selected biogeographic areas

	Species recorded	Endemic species	% endemism
Australia + Tasmania	47	41	87
Mainland Australia	40	25	62
Western Australia	15	4	31
Tasmania	19	7	37
Papua-New Guinea	6	4	66
New Zealand	17	11	65

North American and possibly Australian, and *Paraferrisia podocarpi* is endemic to New Zealand. Evidence from the phylogenetic analysis (Text-fig. 1) indicates that *O. charlesi* is most closely related to the Australian *O. leai*.

Ophelosia crawfordi is distributed through the Australasian region, and is also found in North America. It is host-specific, having been reared only from *Icerya purchasi* and *I. seychellarum*, which argues for an Australian origin. No other species of this genus has been recorded from outside the Australasian or Oriental regions, and it seems clear that *O. crawfordi* is an Australian species which has established in North America as a result of the movement of its host, *I. purchasi*.

Ophelosia keatsi is recorded only from Australian hosts, with the possible exception of *P. affinis*, which may be North American. *O. keatsi* is most closely related to two brachypterous Australian species, according to the consensus cladogram (Text-fig. 1). The available evidence points to *O. keatsi* being of Australian origin.

The conclusion is that all species of *Ophelosia* represented in both New Zealand and Australia are originally Australian, and have been accidentally introduced into New Zealand.

The levels of endemism of Moranilini in selected biogeographic areas are indicated in Table 1.

Faunal relationships

The Moranilini are a monophyletic group with an Australasian, predominantly Australian distribution. Eighty-seven percent of the species and 75% of the genera are found only in Australia. Only two species are known from outside the Australian or Oriental regions; these distributions are almost certainly secondary. There is as yet no record of Moranilini in South America. The only area apart from Australia with a significant number of species is New

Zealand, which has no endemic genera but 65% endemism at the species level.

The common ancestor of the Moranilini probably originated in the Australian area, considering (i) the high level of generic endemism shown by the group, (ii) that almost all the necessary criteria proposed by the dispersal theory of biogeography for a centre of origin (Cranston & Naumann 1991) are met by Australia, and (iii) that the taxa indicated by phylogenetic analysis to be basal to the tribe —*Kneva plana* Bouček, *Amoturella saintpierrei* Girault, and *A*. 'n. sp. 1' (Berry, in prep.)—are all Australian (Text-fig. 1). Bouček (1988a, p. 21) suggested that their radiation in Australasia is because "Australasia, especially Australia, has a rich coccoid fauna (e.g., mealybugs; Williams 1985)," and the eunotines, natural enemies of the Coccoidea, have correspondingly diversified.

The history of the tribe is linked with the geological history of the Australasian region, summarised below.

It is generally accepted that Australia and New Zealand were once a part of Gondwana, joined directly to Antarctica and indirectly to South America, Africa, India and Madagascar. At the beginning of the Cretaceous, 140 mya, the southern supercontinent began to break up. By the middle Lower Cretaceous (120 mya) India, Madagascar, and Africa had begun to separate. At this time New Zealand began to separate from Australia, Antarctica, and South America. The creation of the Tasman Sea was a late Cretaceous event, estimated at 80 mya (Fleming 1975), 78-56 mya (Coleman 1980), and 80–70 mya (Walley & Ross 1991). The precise timing of the loss of land connections between Australia and New Zealand is uncertain, but 80 mya is generally accepted for new sea floor creation and complete continental separation. Australia remained adjacent to Antarctica until 55 mya, and until this time an archipelagic connection probably remained between Australia and South America.

According to Rasnitsyn (1988) the first chalcidoids in the fossil record are late Cretaceous (80 mya), but Poinar (1992) reports chalcidoid wasp inclusions in Lebanese amber (120–130 mya), indicating that the superfamily is at least 120 my old, and probably older, since there are no amber deposits older than 130 mya, and chalcidoids fossilise extremely poorly. Bouček (1988a, p. 22) states that the oldest resins containing pteromalids are 60 my old (Tertiary), and that among the chalcidoids only the pteromalids include groups old enough to have been in existence at the time Gondwana split up; he is apparently excluding the separation of India (140–100 mya, Coleman 1980) and New Zealand (80 mya). Thus Bouček reasons that the only chalcidoid group old enough to have Gondwanic affinities (Australia–South America) are the pteromalids. However, Poinar (1992) reports that the oldest pteromalids found are in Siberian amber, and thus have a minimum age of 78–115 my. On this estimate, the family was probably extant at the time New Zealand began to separate from Gondwana, and almost certainly—as Bouček suggests—present as a family when South America, Antarctica, and Australia diverged. Should endemic moraniline genera be discovered in South America, a minimum age for the tribe of about 55 my would be suggested.

For vicariance to explain the presence of Moranilini in New Zealand, the minimum age of the tribe would have to be 80 my. According to the vicariance theory (Cranston *et al.* 1991), the barrier which divides an ancestral population into incipient species is contemporaneous with the species. This explanation would consequently require some of the ancestral species of present-day New Zealand moranilines to be present at the time land connections to Australia were lost. Considering that the tribe may not have been in existence at that time, this is not likely. Had these species been present, their vicariance, effected by the opening of the Tasman Sea, should have produced a congruent pattern of speciation whose geographical relationships were identical. No such pattern is observable in the New Zealand moranilines (Text-fig. 1).

An explanation which fits the pattern of distribution much better is the occurrence of five dispersal events, involving:

(i) the ancestor of the endemic New Zealand species *Moranila strigaster* and *M. aotearoae* (while relationships within the genus remain unresolved (Text-fig. 1), the most parsimonious explanation is of a single dispersal event);

(ii) *Aphobetus cultratus*, or its ancestor, owing to the sister relationship with *A. goldsmithii* (Girault);

(iii) the ancestor of the clade containing the endemic New Zealand *Aphobetus* species *A. erroli*, *A. maskelli*, *A. paucisetosus*, and *A. nana*, sister group to *A*. 'n. sp. 1' (Berry, in prep.);

(iv) *Aphobetus cyanea* or its ancestor, owing to the sister relationship with *Aphobetus moundi* (Bouček);

(v) the ancestor of the clade containing the endemic New Zealand species *Ophelosia stenopteryx*, *O. mcglashani*, and *O. australis*.

SPECIAL FEATURES OF THE NEW ZEALAND CHALCIDOID FAUNA

According to Bouček (1988a) the New Zealand fauna of chalcidoids is much poorer than in other parts of Australasia. He cites only 14 New Zealand chalcidoid genera as being endemic (about 8%, using Noyes & Valentine's (1989b) estimate of the number of chalcidoid genera in New Zealand), and several other genera as being shared

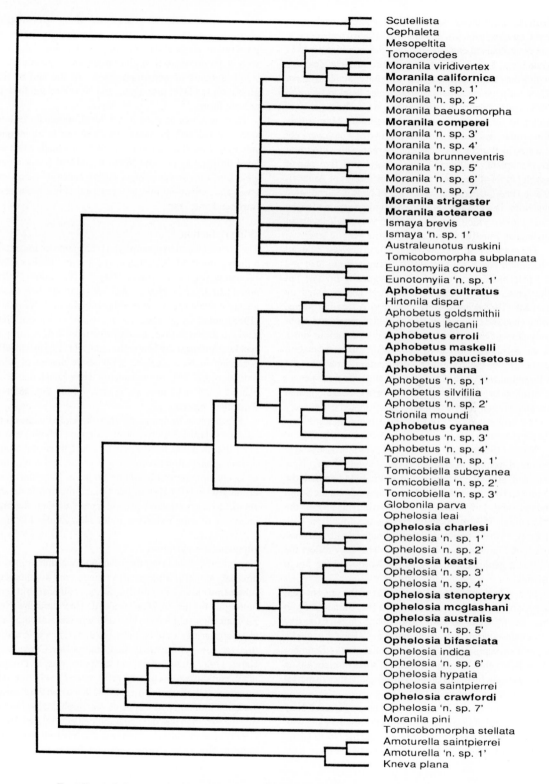

Text-fig. 1 Strict consensus of 309 minimum-length trees for the Moranilini (after Berry 1994); taxa occurring in New Zealand in bold type.

with Australia, though with different species in each country. Conversely, Noyes & Valentine (1989b) consider that the New Zealand chalcidoid fauna shows a high level of endemism, listing 43 genera endemic to New Zealand, which they estimate to be 25% of the total chalcidoid fauna. They estimate endemism at the species level to be up to 50%. The reason for this discrepancy is that the majority of endemic forms occur within the families Mymaridae, Encyrtidae, and Eulophidae, the first two of which were not covered by Bouček's (1988a) opus. Among other groups of Hymenoptera, Naumann (1988) found that five out of seven (71%) of the genera and all the species of Ambositrinae (Proctotrupoidea) occurring in New Zealand were endemic. The Proctotrupoidea are an older group than the chalcidoids, which may explain the very high levels of endemism found in New Zealand at the generic level.

There are several ancestral elements in the New Zealand chalcidoid fauna, for example the family Rotoitidae and the pteromalid genera *Zeala, Fusiterga,* and *Errolia,* but the remaining 10 endemic chalcidoid genera listed by Bouček (1988a) are closely related to Australian forms. Bouček (1988a) considers that the latter genera are probably descendants of forms which arrived at various times from Australia, carried by the wind. This explanation certainly fits the patterns of distribution shown by the Moranilini, with no endemic genera and only three genera sharing species in both regions. Bouček (1988a) suggested that the progeny of the new arrivals speciated extensively in new habitats; to judge by the wide variation in some New Zealand species (see below), this process is still going on.

Noyes (1988) found 44% of the species of Encyrtidae recorded from New Zealand to be endemic. Within New Zealand, 60% of endemic encyrtids are found on both the North and South islands, 25% are found only on the South Island, and 15% only on the North Island. For the Moranilini 55% of endemic species are found on both islands, 45% are found only on the South Island, and none are found only on the North Island. This may reflect the different geological history of the North and the South islands.

In the Oligocene (35–25 mya) most of the present land area of New Zealand was under water (McGlone 1985). In the late Miocene to early Pliocene (5 mya) extensive mountain-building occurred, and New Zealand gained a significant alpine and subalpine habitat. In the Southern Alps these habitats became centres of speciation for alpine flora, perhaps by plants derived by long-distance dispersal from Australia (Raven 1973).

At the end of the Pliocene a glaciation bisected New Zealand north of Cook Strait, leaving the South Island with a predominantly alpine environment and the North Island with mainly temperate forest. Since that time there have

been approximately 20 glaciations, along with marked changes of sea level. At the time of the final glaciation sea level fell by about 200 m, creating a continuous landmass with a predominantly alpine/subalpine vegetation and small amounts of temperate forest. At the end of this glaciation sea level rose again, and New Zealand took its present form.

Thus, at times of rises in sea level, mountain refugia were created and the biota were reduced to alpine and subalpine forms, which recolonised the lowlands when sea level dropped again. The North Island had fewer alpine areas and thus fewer refugia during times of rising sea level, and extinctions may account for the presence here of fewer endemic taxa.

Wing reduction

The New Zealand hymenopteran fauna appears to contain a high proportion of flightless species, or species which have some flightless members. Noyes & Valentine (1989a) noted that amongst New Zealand Mymaridae 40% of the genera include species with abbreviated wings. Naumann (1988) noted wing reduction in 89% of species of New Zealand Ambositrinae, as compared to 66% of Australian species. Amongst the Moranilini, only 11% of the species occurring in New Zealand show some degree of wing reduction, but 36% of the endemic New Zealand species exhibit wing reduction, as against 7% of the endemic Australian species.

Brachyptery or aptery is often associated with alpine habitats (Mani 1968). Noyes & Valentine (1989a) speculated that in dense habitats such as leaf litter and alpine tussock grasses flight is not advantageous, and wings may be an encumbrance to searching for hosts. Recolonisation of the lowlands by taxa isolated in mountain refugia and subject to such selective pressures may explain the high incidence of wing reduction in the New Zealand fauna.

Intraspecific variation

Noyes (1988) listed a number of authors who have noted an unusual amount of intraspecific variation in Thysanoptera, Ichneumonidae, Proctotrupoidea, and carabid and mordellid beetles in New Zealand. He found the New Zealand encyrtid fauna to be extremely variable, the variation appearing not to be linked to geographical distribution, including altitude, except in one species. Conversely, Harris (1987) found variation in spider wasps (Pompilidae), particularly in colour pattern, to be closely linked to distribution. LaSalle & Boler (1994) discussed the extreme variation found in a new species of eulophid, also finding that the variation was not geographically correlated. Berry (1994) carried out morphometric analyses on the world fauna of Moranilini (64 species), and showed that the most variable were the New Zealand species *Aphobetus maskelli* and *A. cyanea*.

Naumann (1988) found sexual dimorphism to be very pronounced in New Zealand Ambositrinae, particularly amongst wing-reduced taxa. Sexual dimorphism is a form of intraspecific variation very common in Hymenoptera, owing to a difference in selection pressures operating on males and females (Gauld & Bolton 1988). In the eunotines many characters are sexually dimorphic—for example, the form of the antennae, which in females are specialised for host location. Coloration and morphometric characters are also highly sexually dimorphic.

Sculpture, the most constant of the morphological characters, is sometimes the only clue to association of the sexes. However, in very small males the microsculptural patterns are sometimes disturbed: see Fig. M28 and M29, showing the propodeal sculpture of two male specimens of *Ophelosia charlesi*, offspring of the same female. The difference in sculpture correlates with a marked difference in size.

RELEVANCE OF MORANILINI TO HORTICULTURE IN NEW ZEALAND

Most of the mealybugs (Coccoidea: Pseudococcidae) known from New Zealand are indigenous, but the major pests are introduced species of the genus *Pseudococcus* (Charles 1989). *P. longispinus*, *P. calceolariae*, and *P. affinis* are pests of a wide variety of horticultural crops and ornamentals. All three are probably Australian, although there is some disagreement about the origin of *P. affinis*. According to Cox (1987) it is almost certainly a North American species, while Williams (1985) considers it to be Australian in origin. These mealybugs are not an economic problem in Australia unless the natural enemies presumed to be controlling their populations are disrupted by pesticides (J. G. Charles, pers. comm.; Williams 1985). Thus Australia is an appropriate place to search for organisms for introduction into New Zealand as biological control agents. In order for a biological control programme to be carried out most effectively, it is necessary to know both (i) the identity of the natural enemies in the pest's endemic area and (ii) whether any or all of these natural enemies are already present in the area where the organism is a pest.

The genus *Ophelosia* in Australia has for some time been known to include species which prey on pseudococcid eggs (Wilson 1963), and which would be possible candidates for mealybug biocontrol in New Zealand. However, the host relationships and taxonomy of the genus were not well known in Australia, and although *Ophelosia* was known to be present in New Zealand (Valentine 1967), the identity

and number of species present were unknown. The most recent catalogue (Valentine & Walker 1991) recorded only five species of Eunotinae from New Zealand (*Aphobetus maskelli*, *Modronila cyanea*, *M. californica*, *Moranila comperei*, and *Pidinka nana*), and the record of *M. comperei* was based on a misidentification.

This revision records 17 eunotine species from New Zealand, among which are seven species of *Ophelosia*, three endemic and four Australian in origin. None of the endemic species have reliable host records, nor are they likely to be effective against *Pseudococcus*, since their distribution (*O. australis*, Map 11; *O. mcglashani*, Map 16; *O. stenopteryx*, Map 17) is typical of species with endemic hosts. The Australian species present in New Zealand are *Ophelosia bifasciata*, *O. charlesi*, *O. crawfordi*, and *O. keatsi*. Charles (1993) recorded *Ophelosia* sp. A and sp. B from mealybugs in New Zealand. His material was examined as part of the present study; sp. A was found to be *O. bifasciata*, and sp. B *O. charlesi*.

The following Australian species of *Ophelosia* are natural enemies of the three important New Zealand pest species of *Pseudococcus*:

    P. affinis   : *charlesi, keatsi*
    P. calceolariae : *bifasciata, charlesii*
    P. longispinus : *bifasciata, charlesii, keatsi*

O. bifasciata was recorded as a solitary parasitoid of *P. longispinus* and *P. calceolariae*, in one instance as a hyperparasitoid of *Anagyrus fusciventris* (Encyrtidae) in *P. longispinus*, and also as a predator of *P. calceolariae* ovisacs. *O. charlesi* was recorded as a solitary parasitoid of *P. longispinus* and *P. calceolariae* and, most commonly, as a gregarious egg predator in ovisacs of *P. calceolariae* and *P. affinis*. *O. keatsi* was reared from *P. longispinus* and from *P. affinis*, but the feeding habits are unknown. These species of *Ophelosia* are already present in New Zealand, almost certainly having been introduced along with their hosts on plant material. *Aphobetus nana*, endemic to New Zealand, has also been reared from *Pseudococcus longispinus*.

Smith & Compere (1931) reported that live *O. crawfordi* collected by Flanders in Australia from *Planococcus citri* ovisacs and from the mummies of an unidentified species of *Pseudococcus* (presumably as a hyperparasitoid) were sent to California, where they were reared on the ovisacs of unidentified mealybugs. The reared specimens were not released. Wilson (1963) identified *Ophelosia crawfordi* as a common natural enemy of *P. longispinus* (as *P. adonidum* L.) in Australia. Charles (1989) mentioned this latter reference and recommended the description and characterisation of the New Zealand species of *Ophelosia*, and their comparison to *O. crawfordi* as a mealybug parasitoid. In fact *O. crawfordi* is not common, nor has it been reliably recorded as an enemy of any pseudococcid, so it is likely that both these records (Smith & Compere 1931, Wilson 1963) are based on misidentifications. *O. crawfordi* has been recorded from New Zealand only once, so it is dubious whether it has established here. In any case, the results of this study show that it is specific to *Icerya*, and since this genus is already under effective biological control in New Zealand (Morales & Bain 1989) there is no necessity for further introductions of natural enemies.

Other pest or possible pest coccoid species which have natural enemies within the Moranilini are discussed below.

Phenacoccus graminicola, a grass-feeding mealybug, is an occasional pest of fruit trees in New Zealand. *O. charlesi* has been reared from its ovisacs, and *O. keatsi* has been reared, presumably as a primary parasitoid.

Planococcus citri, an important pest of citrus overseas, is frequently intercepted in New Zealand but is not an established pest. *O. bifasciata* and *O. indica* have been recorded as natural enemies.

Icerya purchasi is not a problem in New Zealand, being under effective control since the introduction of *Rodolia cardinalis* and *Cryptochetum iceryae*, both Australian natural enemies (Morales & Bain 1989). Should these prove ineffective in the future, *Ophelosia hypatia* and *O. crawfordi* would be ideal candidates for importation.

Black scale, *Saissetia oleae*, is a minor pest in New Zealand (Morales 1989). *Moranila californica* has been recorded as a parasitoid, but *Scutellista cyanea* is much more common. This latter species has been introduced into New Zealand several times but has failed to establish.

All the species of *Ophelosia* known to be natural enemies of pest mealybugs in New Zealand are well established, hence further introductions are unneccessary, unless different strains which are more vigorous, or have slightly different host ranges, are present in Australia. *Ophelosia bifasciata* was first recorded in New Zealand in 1966, *O. charlesi* in 1925, and *O. keatsi* in 1963. The single record of *O. bifasciata* as a hyperparasitoid suggests that it may develop as an egg predator in unparasitised mealybug populations, but it may be a facultative hyperparasitoid of encyrtid primary parasitoids in parasitised populations. Charles (1993) suggests that *O. bifasciata* and *O. charlesi* may be desirable egg predators but undesirable hyperparasitoids, but there is no evidence that *O. charlesii* acts as a hyperparasitoid.

The Australian species of *Ophelosia* for which no host records exist are *leai* Dodd, *saintpierrei* Girault, 'n. sp. 3,' 'n. sp. 4,' 'n. sp. 5,' 'n. sp. 6,' and 'n. sp. 7' (Berry, in prep.). Any of these would be worthy of further investigation as candidates for biological control of *Pseudococcus* in New Zealand, but *O. leai* is of particular interest, for the following reasons.

(i) It is commonly collected. If this means that it has a broad range of hosts, it would be unsuitable for introduction as a biological control agent. However, it may be specific to a relatively commonly occurring host such as *P. longispinus*, *P. affinis*, or *P. calceolariae*, in which case it would be a possible candidate for introduction.

(ii) According to a phylogenetic analysis of the tribe (Text-fig. 1), *O. leai* is most closely related to a clade including *O. charlesi*, which is an egg predator of several species of *Pseudococcus*.

Other Australian natural enemies of *P. longispinus*, *P. affinis*, and *P. calceolariae* include the encyrtids *Tetracnemoidea brevicornis* (Girault), *Parectromoides varipes* (Girault), *T. sydneyensis* (Timberlake), and *Anagyrus fusciventris* (Girault). All four species are known to be present in New Zealand (Charles 1993), though *A. fusciventris* has been collected only from the Auckland area and only very recently. Charles (1993) recommends its distribution throughout the rest of New Zealand to enhance control. *Coccophagus gurneyi* Compere was introduced from Australia to the U.S.A. and from there to New Zealand, where it is now widespread (Charles 1989).

According to Charles (1993) the encyrtids listed above and *C. gurneyi* are the most effective natural enemies of the pest species *P. longispinus* and *P. calceolariae*, and since they are already present in New Zealand, classical biocontrol programmes against these two mealybugs need not be considered.

Since no encyrtids have been reared from *P. affinis* in New Zealand, Charles (1993) recommends evaluation of *Pseudaphycus maculipennis* (Mercet), a Mediterranean species, for introduction against *P. affinis* on the grounds that it has provided control in the south of France.

MATERIALS AND METHODS

The Moranilini are reasonably large chalcidoids, ranging from slightly less than 1 mm long (*Aphobetus nana*) to almost 3 mm long (*A. cyanea*). They are also relatively heavily sclerotised and non-collapsing; accordingly most specimens were examined dry on points. Point-mounting was preferred to Noyes's (1988) method of card-mounting, since it was extremely difficult to examine and measure some characters in card-mounted specimens. (Card-mounting does however provide much more protection.)

Specimens to be mounted were relaxed, and the wings were set (spread to expose the dorsum) on non-porous card. Mounting was done at low magnification under a stereo microscope. Specimens for examination under the compound microscope were mounted on microscope slides using Noyes's (1988) technique. Body parts for drawing were cleared in KOH (except wings) and mounted on microscope slides in Hoyer's solution. Drawings were made with a drawing tube on a Wild Leitz compound microscope.

Micrographs were taken on a JEOL JSM-35C Scanning Electron Microscope at Black Mountain Laboratories, Division of Entomology, CSIRO. All specimens were point-mounted and placed in a small, rotatable, tiltable vice which allowed them to be viewed at several different angles (unlike the usual mounting procedure involving brass stubs). Specimens were prepared for SEM by washing in household detergent solution and air-drying at 21°C for less than 24 hours.

Absolute measurements were not used. Relative morphometric measurements were made using a light microscope and a micrometer, and checked using the calibrating facility on the JEOL 6400 machine at the Research School of Biological Sciences, Australian National University. Measurements were found to be accurate to within 0.01–0.001 mm (for example, the same distance measured by micrometer was 0.243 mm and by SEM calibration 0.249 mm). Ranges for measurements were achieved by measuring a sample of at least 10 specimens of each sex (where possible).

Collecting was by netting and by host collection and rearing. Hosts were held in ventilated plastic pots under ambient conditions until parasitoids emerged.

Format of descriptions

Authorship and *family affiliation* are given at the first mention of a taxon in the text. Authorities and families are not cited under 'Material examined' since this information is a summary of label data.

Type details. Sex and deposition of the type specimen are stated. The label details are given verbatim under "Label data". Type labels by the present author are not quoted, but all follow the form "TYPE, species name, authority, designated J. A. Berry, date." All information on one label is enclosed by quotation marks, and the information on each line of the label is separated by a slash (/). Details are given in this format only for type material which has been seen by the author. If type material has not been seen, this is explicitly stated. The publication details are given under 'Publication data' where relevant.

Females for all species are described or redescribed in the same format. Measurements are presented as ranges, with means in parentheses. Microsculpture terms follow Harris (1979). Bouček (1988a) criticises this system as having too many terms that are not descriptive enough; however, for the purposes of this work it was quite suitable.

Males. Only character states which differ from those found in the female are listed.

Material examined. All New Zealand specimens examined are listed by area code; details of the New Zealand system of area codes are given in Crosby *et al.* (1976). Areas are cited geographically, i.e., north to south, beginning with ND (Northland) and ending with SI (Stewart Island). All label data are given, in abbreviated form, including collector(s), date of collection, and hosts.

Biology. All records are from specimens examined in the present study unless otherwise specified.

Distribution. All areas/ states/ countries from which the species is recorded are listed. 'Australia' refers to a distribution anywhere within Australia, including Tasmania. 'Mainland Australia' excludes Tasmania. The expression 'eastern Australia' refers to any or all states east of Western Australia.

Collectors

JAdB	J. A. deBoer (ex DSIR)
ZB	Zdenek Bouček (BMNH)
JGC	John Charles (HortResearch)
JWE	John Early (LUNZ)
ESG	E. Gourlay (Cawthron Institute)
GK	Willy Kuschel (ex DSIR)
PAM	Peter Maddison (ex Landcare Research)
JSN	John Noyes (BMNH)
GWR	Graeme Ramsay (ex Landcare Research)
EWV	Errol Valentine (ex DSIR)
AKW	Annette Walker (IIEL).

Repositories (abbreviations follow Watt 1979)

ANIC	Australian National Insect Collection, CSIRO, Canberra, Australia
BMNH	British Museum (Natural History), London, U.K. (= The Natural History Museum)
BPBM	Bernice P. Bishop Museum, Honolulu, Hawai'i, U.S.A.
DSIR	Department of Scientific and Industrial Research, New Zealand (now defunct)
IIEL	International Institute of Entomology, London, U.K.
LUNZ	Lincoln University, Canterbury, N.Z.
MVMA	Museum of Victoria, Melbourne, Victoria, Australia
NZAC	New Zealand Arthropod Collection, Landcare Research, Auckland, N.Z.
QMBA	Queensland Museum, Brisbane, Australia
SAMA	South Australian Museum, Adelaide, South Australia
USNM	United States National Museum, Washington, D.C., U.S.A.
WARI	Waite Agricultural Research Institute, University of Adelaide, South Australia

TAXONOMIC FEATURES

A representative from each of the New Zealand genera of Moranilini is illustrated in Fig. 1–3. Morphological terms used here generally follow Bouček (1988a); the principal terms are defined briefly below, and illustrated in Fig. 4 and 5. Antennae and forewings are featured in Fig. 6–30, and SEM studies appear as Fig. M1–M36.

HEAD

Vertex: top of head.
Occiput: area between vertex and foramen.
Occipital carina: carinate upper occipital margin.
OD (ocular diameter): longest axis of posterior ocelli.
OOL (ocular-ocellar line): shortest distance between posterior ocelli and eye.
Face: front of head, merging dorsally with vertex and delimited ventrally by clypeal margin and genal carina.
Face length: length from vertex to genal carina with head in full facial view.
Face width: measured at widest point with head in full facial view.
Gena: area between eye and mandibles (sometimes termed 'malar space'), delimited posteriorly in this group by the *genal carina*.
Malar space: minimum distance between eye and mouth margin.
Malar groove: groove running from lower margin of eye to mouth margin.
Toruli: antennal insertions or sockets; distance between toruli and clypeal margin is measured from ventral margin of torulus.
Scrobes: more or less depressed area above toruli; may be margined dorsally by a weak or strong carina.

ANTENNAE

Sensilla: sense organs occurring on some or all funicular segments and club. Two forms occur in the Moranilini: (a) *placoid longitudinal sensilla* – correctly referred to as 'multiporous plate sensilla' (Bouček 1988a) – attached to antennal surface by an elongate base, but with a tapering apex free above surface, and (b) *trichoid sensilla*, modified longitudinal sensilla with a very short base but greatly lengthened free apex.
Scape: first antennal segment, jointed in the socket (torulus) by the radicula (not counted as a segment).
Pedicel: second antennal segment, elongate pyriform.
Funicle: consists of five segments in females and four in males; these segments are referred to as F1 to F4 or F5 from base to apex of funicle.
Club: last three flagellar segments, separated by partial or complete sutures.

THORAX

The term 'thorax' is used to describe the median part of the body, excluding the propodeum. It is thus not equivalent to the term 'mesosoma.'
Pronotum: broader than long, with undifferentiated regular setation; and with or without a row of long setae on posterior margin (=*setal ring*).
Mesonotum: divided into several parts. Anterior to *transscutal line* is the *mesoscutum*, in turn subdivided into a middle lobe and two lateral *scapulae* by the *notauli*. Posterior to transcutal line are the *scutellum* and laterally the *axillae*. The scutellum may have a *frenal area* delimited apically.
Metanotum: divided into a medial *dorsellum* and *dorsellar fovea* and a lateral *metanotal furrow*.
Mesopleuron: includes a *subalar area* from which an oblique groove (*pleural suture*) runs to the middle coxa. The *mesepimeron* is above the pleural suture and the *mesepisternum* below it.

FOREWINGS

In many small parasitic Hymenoptera the wing venation is very reduced and a simplified nomenclature is used. From the base of the wing the veins are *submarginal, marginal,* and *postmarginal*; the *stigmal* vein branches posteriorly from the junction of the marginal and postmarginal veins. The stigmal vein may be knobbed apically (*stigma*), and this in turn may send off a stub (the *uncus*) towards the postmarginal vein.

The measurements of the ratios marginal : stigmal vein length and postmarginal : stigmal vein length are detailed in Fig. 5. Goulet & Huber (1993) note that the names of these veins do not connote any homology with similarly named veins in other groups of Hymenoptera, but are simply a convenient reference system.

Other features of the wing (all on the dorsal surface, unless otherwise specified) are:
Costal cell: the area between the submarginal vein and the costal edge of the wing.
Ventral setal row: row of setae on ventral surface of costal cell; may be complete or broadly or narrowly interrupted.
Basal cell: area bounded by submarginal vein, basal vein, and *cubital hairline*.
Cubital hairline: pilose area on cubital vein, posterior boundary of basal cell.
Basal hairline: pilose area on basal vein, distal boundary of basal cell.
Parastigma: thickening at distal end of submarginal vein; may be extended down basal vein.
Speculum and **linea calva:** two bare areas in the usually undifferentiated pilosity distal of the basal vein. Bouček (1988a) defines the speculum as a bare area immediately

beyond the basal cell, and the linea calva as "an oblique bare strip further distad, towards the stigmal vein." Gauld & Bolton (1988) define the speculum as a bare area running obliquely from the parastigma (the intercept of the submarginal vein between basal and marginal veins) to the hind region of the wing, and the linea calva as running from the stigmal vein to the hind margin. Thus the two features are defined on their position relative to the parastigma and the stigmal vein respectively, and the inference is also that the speculum is immediately distal of the basal vein and the linea calva is not.

In the Eunotini the width of the primary bare area or speculum ranges from very narrow to very wide, reaching past the stigmal vein. Using the Gauld & Bolton definition this feature cannot be classified as a speculum, since it reaches the stigmal vein; nor as a linea calva, since it is immediately adjacent to the basal vein. In my opinion it is probably both, with a secondary loss of the setae dividing the two areas, but this is purely speculative. For the purpose of coding these characters, the Bouček (1988a) definition was used.

Stigmal area: triangular area in the forewing between the postmarginal and stigmal veins.

LEGS

From the base, the legs are made up of the *coxa*, the *trochanter*, the *trochantellus*, the *femur*, the *tibia*, and the *tarsus*. The apex of the hind tibia has a single spur or two spurs, and these are measured against the length of the first hind tarsal segment, the *basitarsus*.

PROPODEUM

The *propodeum* is the first segment of the metasoma, incorporated into the thorax. A *nucha* or neck may be formed by a narrowed medial area before the apex. Carination present may include a longitudinal *median carina*, sublateral longitudinal *plicae*, or a medial transverse carina, the *costula*.

GASTER

The term 'gaster' is used in the sense of Bouček, i.e., the metasoma not including the first metasomal segment (the propodeum), which is treated separately.

T1: first dorsal segment (tergite) of gaster (second metasomal tergite).

S1: first ventral segment (sternite) of gaster (second metasomal sternite).

Genitalia: male genitalia are very rarely used in pteromalid taxonomy. In females the ovipositing apparatus is derived from the ventral parts of the sixth and seventh gastral segments, and is connected with the *epipygium* or fused seventh and eighth tergites.

KEY TO MORANILINI
KNOWN FROM NEW ZEALAND
(females and males)

1 Propodeum with median carina developed into a tooth (Fig. M3, M4, M7, M8, M12, M13); frenal area sometimes delimited by a groove or a line of punctations (Fig. M1, M3) ... genus *Aphobetus* .. 3
—Propodeum without a tooth developed from median carina (Fig. M21, M25, M27–29) ... 2

2(1) Propodeum with median carina and costula complete (Fig. M21); setae at base of gaster in a compact tuft (Fig. M17–19) ... genus *Moranila* .. 8

—Propodeum reticulate, with median carina developed only at anterior end, costula absent (Fig. M25, M27–29); setae at base of gaster not in a compact tuft (Fig. M25–29, M32) ... genus *Ophelosia* .. 11

Aphobetus (p. 20)

3(1) Basal cell of forewing completely setose, with linea calva the only bare patch (Fig. 20); large, metallic blue species ... (p. 23) .. *cyanea*
—Basal cell with scattered setae or bare, with speculum present (Fig. 19, 21) ... 4

4(1) Notauli replaced by a wide, shallow groove (Fig. M1) ... (p. 22) .. *cultratus*
—Notauli not in the form of a wide, shallow groove (Fig. M3, M7, M12) ... 5

5(4) Frenum delimited by just a faint line or a change in sculpture (Fig. M7, M8, M12) ... 6
—Frenum delimited by an indented groove (e.g., Fig. M1, M3) ... 7

6(5) Thorax not depressed; scutellum at least slightly convex in lateral aspect; more than 4 setae in pronotal ring ... (p. 25) .. *erroli*
—Thorax depressed; scutellum flat in lateral aspect; 4 setae in pronotal ring ... (p. 28) .. *nana*

7(5) Pronotum with more than 4 setae in ring ... (p. 26) .. *maskelli*
—Pronotum with 4 setae in ring ... (p. 29) .. *paucisetosus*

Moranila (p. 31)

8(2) Forewings reduced, reaching just beyond propodeum (Fig. 22) ... (p. 32) .. *aotearoae*
—Forewings reaching at least halfway down gaster (Fig. 23) ... 9

9(8) T1 longitudinally striate over most of surface (cf. Fig. M11) ... (p. 37) .. *strigaster*
—T1 smooth ... 10

10(9) Setal bases on pronotum and mesoscutum conspicuously reticulate; propodeum without a conspicuous triangular plate at base of median carina; sensilla on male antenna shorter than flagellar segments; S1 with medial area wide, flat, pitted (Fig. M17) ... (p. 33) .. *californica*
—Setal bases on pronotum and mesoscutum not conspicuously reticulate; propodeum with a conspicuous triangular plate at base of median carina; sensilla on male antennae longer than flagellar segments (Fig. 13); S1 with 2 rows of foveae anteriorly, separated by narrow ridges (Fig. M18) ... (p. 35) .. *comperei*

Ophelosia (p. 38)

11(2) Antennal scrobes transversely striate (Fig. M31); propodeal nucha longer than broad ... (p. 44) .. *crawfordi*
—Antennal scrobes smooth (Fig. M23); propodeal nucha square or broader than long (Fig. M25, M27–29) ... 12

12(11) Wings reduced; occipital carina weak ... 13
—Wings reaching end of gaster or beyond; occipital carina weak or strong ... 14

13(12) Female forewing with basal hairline not infumate, disc with less than 10 setae, and no rudimentary stigmal vein (Fig. 25) ... (p. 39) .. *australis*
—Female forewing with basal hairline infumate, disc with about 40 setae, and rudimentary stigmal vein present (Fig. 29); male unknown ... (p. 47) .. *mcglashani*

14(12) Wing long but narrow (Fig. 30); occipital carina weak; ocelli removed from occiput by one ocellar diameter ... (p. 48) .. *stenopteryx*
—Wing of normal width (Fig. 26–28); occipital carina strong; ocelli removed from occiput by less than half an ocellar diameter ... 15

15(14) Setal tuft on forewing thick, strong, triangular, composed of setae as long as proximal submarginal setae ... (p. 40) .. *bifasciata*
—Setae on basal hairline forming a line, strip, or tuft but always shorter than proximal submarginal setae ... 16

16(15) Antennal scrobes weakly carinate; female cubital hairline absent; M:S ratio <2.5 (Fig. 26); male cubital hairline present (Fig. 27) ... (p. 42) .. *charlesi*
—Antennal scrobes not carinate; female cubital hairline partly present; M:S ratio >3 (Fig. 28); male cubital hairline absent ... (p. 46) .. *keatsi*

DESCRIPTIONS

Genus *Aphobetus* Howard

Aphobetus Howard, 1896: 166. Ashmead 1904: 328. Bouček 1988a: 363. Type species *Aphobetus maskelli* Howard, by original monotypy.

Muscideopsis Girault, 1915a: 324. Type species *Muscideopsis goldsmithii* Girault, by original designation. Synonymised by Bouček (1988a: 363).

Austroeunotus Girault, 1938: 84–85. Type species *Austroeunotus silvifilia* Girault, by original designation. Synonymised by Bouček (1988a: 363).

Pidinka Bouček, 1988a: 362. Type species *Pidinka nana* Bouček, by monotypy and original designation. New synonymy.

Modronila Bouček, 1988a: 364. Type species *Modronila cyanea* Bouček, by monotypy and original designation. New synonymy.

Female. Head brown-black to shiny black, with or without metallic lustre; dorsal margin weakly to strongly concave. Face 1.1–1.8× broader than long. Occiput strongly to weakly margined; back of head posterior to carina variously sculptured. Posterior ocelli crossing edge of carina, or removed by less than 1 ocellar diameter. Ocelli clear to red; OD from 0.35 OOL to almost equal to OOL. Eyes minutely hairy. Face and vertex smooth to variously sculptured, with scattered setae, these long on vertex.

Antennal insertions from slightly less than 1 torular diameter to 2 torular diameters above clypeal margin; scrobes either smooth and unsculptured or finely striate centrally, very weakly or not carinate anteriorly. Antennae yellow to dark brown, unicolorous or not; scape not extending to vertex; pedicel longer than F1; funicular segments increasing in width if not in length towards club; F1 not broader than long; remaining funicular segments varying. Club ovoid, 0.4–0.9× as long as funicle. Malar groove complete and conspicuous to almost entirely absent. Genae weakly to strongly carinate; groove relatively wide, striate or not. Oral margin between toruli straight, sloping down to offset genal carina. Mandible with lower tooth broad, pointed, upper tooth blunt and undivided, or divided into 2 or 3 blunt or pointed teeth.

Thorax shiny, black to dark brown, without metallic lustre. Pronotum much broader than long, narrower than mesoscutum, sculptured, with a transverse ring of 4–12 conspicuous setae ranging from weak and brown to strong and black, with scattered short setae anterior to setal ring, smooth and shiny posterior to ring. Mesoscutum smooth and shiny to finely reticulate or finely transversely rugose. Notauli ranging from broad shallow grooves to complete, composed of a series of small, well defined pits reaching scutellar boundary. Scapulae smooth and shiny to finely transversely rugose, reticulate, or finely longitudinally striate. Scutellum longer than broad to broader than long, convex to flat in lateral aspect, with 2 pairs of setae; posterior third usually divided by frenal line or indented frenal groove consisting of a row of punctures; upper part usually more heavily sculptured than lower part. Axillae sculptured or not, with scattered setae. Mesepisternum centrally with a depressed, finely striate to smooth, elongate triangular area; upper and lower mesepimeron variously sculptured. Dorsellum triangular, sculptured or not; remainder of metanotum variously sculptured.

Forewing hyaline or infumate. Marginal vein 1.25–5.8× as long as stigmal vein. Postmarginal vein as long as stigmal vein or slightly longer. Stigmal area bare to setose. Costal cell straight or excised at apex, margined with a varying number of setae, and with a continuous row of ventral setae and other setation. Submarginal vein not smoothly contiguous with marginal vein, with varying number of setae. Proximal part of wing completely setose (excepting linea calva) to bare, excepting basal and cubital hairlines; distal part with fine, close setation.

Legs from yellow to dark brown, with tarsal claws dark. Hind coxae with or without dorsal and lateral crests of setae. One or 2 tibial spurs present, the longest from 0.1× hind basitarsus to almost as long.

Propodeum ranging from dark yellow-brown, often brown-black anteriorly, to dark red or black, with or without metallic lustre, broad at spiracles, narrowing into a very short, fairly broad neck, and with a strong anteromedial tooth (expanded median carina). Costula and plica present; additional median plicae (complete or incomplete) present or absent. Basal fovea inconspicuous or deep; apical fovea present or absent. Tooth smooth or sculptured, sometimes delimited by longitudinal or oblique carinae on either side.

Gaster unicolorous pale to bright yellow through dark yellow-brown to dark brown or black with metallic lustre, with coloration often graduated towards apex and base. T1 0.4–0.95x as long as gaster, mostly unsculptured, but with longitudinal striations in one species; a loose tuft of setae or several long setae present at base, not extended down margin of fovea. Ovipositor short, scarcely extending beyond tip of gaster. S1 variously sculptured, its surface finely striate or rarely smooth or alveolate; setae absent.

Male. As for female, except as follows.

Head shiny black to shiny dark brown or red-brown, with or without metallic lustre. Antennal insertions 2–3 torular diameters above clypeal margin; funicular segments nodose, separated by distinct constrictions and with long setae, with F1 usually the longest; club as long as F1 to twice as long.

Thorax shiny, black to dark brown. Forewing hyaline or with a faint infumate patch posterior to marginal, stigmal, and/or postmarginal veins. Marginal vein 1.6–4.9× as long as stigmal vein. Postmarginal vein slightly longer than stigmal vein. Basal hairline pigmented or not, with a line of setae; basal cell margined by cubital hairline.

Gaster more slender than in female; T1 0.3–0.7× as long as gaster.

Biology. *Aphobetus* species are parasitoids or hyperparasitoids of Coccoidea or Aphididae; rearing records suggest little host specificity. *A. maskelli* has been reared as a parasitoid of Pseudococcidae, Diaspididae, Coccidae, Eriococcidae, and Aphididae; and as a hyperparasitoid on coccids or eriococcids via encyrtids. All other host records for species of *Aphobetus* fall into the above families.

Distribution. *Aphobetus* occurs in Australia and New Zealand, without overlap of species. Six species are endemic to New Zealand; two species are endemic to Tasmania, and the remaining six to Australia.

Remarks. When Bouček (1988a) synonymised *Muscideopsis* and *Austroeunotus* with *Aphobetus* he used four character states, taken from the generic description and the key, to define the genus *Aphobetus*. Berry (1994) found most of these character states to be highly homoplasious, accepting only the presence of a propodeal tooth as an apomorphy defining the monophyletic group (*Aphobetus* + *Modronila* + *Pidinka* + *Strionila*). *Pidinka* and *Modronila* are accordingly here synonymised with *Aphobetus*. (The synonymy of *Strionila* is discussed in Berry (in prep.)). The key character states for each of Bouček's genera are discussed below, following the phylogenetic analysis carried out by Berry (1994).

Aphobetus. Bouček (1988a) used the following key character states to define the genus *Aphobetus*.
(i) Marginal vein less than 3× as long as stigmal vein. This character was found to be highly variable within species, and to overlap considerably between species. Berry (1994) was not able to devise an appropriate method for coding the character into states, and it was not included in her analysis, although it was used in some species diagnoses.
(ii) Propodeum with strong anteromedian tooth and additional sculpture. This state is a synapomorphy for the entire *Aphobetus* group (*Aphobetus* + *Modronila* + *Pidinka* + *Strionila*), according to Berry's (1994) analysis. The sculpture of the propodeum is an extremely important character in the Moranilini, and one of the weaknesses of Berry's

analysis is that only two characters were encoded from the propodeum.

(iii) Scutellum in posterior half with a distinct frenal cross-groove or cross-line of punctures. Bouček used this character to define the group *Aphobetus*, *Strionila*, and *Modronila*, excluding *Pidinka*, in his generic key. *P. nana* and *A. erroli* both lack a frenal cross-groove. According to Berry's analysis this is due to a reversal, and the absence of this character state in the above two species should not be used to remove them from the monophyletic *Aphobetus* group. This character state also appears convergently in the Australian species *Moranila* 'n. sp. 6' (Berry, in prep.).

(iv) Hind coxa dorsally bare and shiny, rarely slightly pilose. Although Bouček (1988a) uses this character state in his definition of the genus *Aphobetus*, it occurs in only three of the ten species of *Aphobetus*, sensu Bouček. *Strionila* and *Modronila* also lack dorsal pilosity on the hind coxa. The remaining seven species of *Aphobetus* sensu Bouček, plus *Pidinka nana* and *A. erroli* (*Pidinka* sensu Bouček) have dorsal pilosity in this area. Obviously, this character is highly homoplasious in the group, and is not useful in indicating genus-level relationships.

Modronila. Bouček used the following key character states to define his monotypic genus *Modronila*: (i) forewing proximally with dense pilosity; (ii) linea calva alone present, no speculum; (iii) marginal vein almost 4x as long as stigmal vein. These three wing characters are autapomorphies, and cannot be used to deduce relationship. The form of S1 is also autapomorphic. *Modronila* is a highly derived, endemic New Zealand form of *Aphobetus*.

Strionila. Bouček used the following key character states to define the monotypic genus *Strionila*. (i) First tergite with a transverse area of longitudinal striae on disc. This state is an autapomorphy and is not useful for deriving relationships. It has also arisen independently in one New Zealand species of *Moranila*, *M. strigaster*. (ii) "Punctate frenal groove coarse, and delimited posteriorly by a slight carina" (p. 288). Although the punctations are coarser than those found in *Aphobetus* sensu Bouček and in *Modronila*, I can see no evidence of the slight carina claimed by Bouček. The form of S1 is also autapomorphic. *Strionila* is a derived West Australian form of *Aphobetus*.

Pidinka. Bouček distinguished his monotypic genus *Pidinka* using the following character states. (i) "Propodeum with broad triangular tooth raised towards middle (suggesting broad median carina), its sides formed by transverse costula, without grid-like sculpture" (p. 229). I can see no major difference in the form of the propodeal tooth in *Pidinka* as compared to the other members of *Aphobetus* (see Fig. M3, M4, M7, M8, M12, M13). (ii) "Base of gaster on sides with loose hair" (Bouček 1988a, p.

229). I found the setosity at the base of the gaster to be the same in *Pidinka*, and all but three species of *Aphobetus* in the sense of Bouček. The character state is not diagnostic of any grouping. (iii) Hind coxa dorsally with short, curved pilosity. See state (iv) under *Aphobetus*. (iv) Thorax dorsally depressed. This is an autapomorphy. *Pidinka* is an endemic New Zealand form of *Aphobetus* most closely related to *A. erroli*, which is intermediate in several character states between Bouček's concepts of the two genera.

Aphobetus cultratus new species

Fig. 6, 19, M1, M2; Map 1

Female. Head shiny black; dorsal margin slightly concave. Face 1.3–1.5(1.41)× broader than long. Occipital carina strong; back of head longitudinally striate laterally, interrupted medially. Ocelli clear; OD 0.6× OOL. Vertex with long dark setae; frons with strong, dark setae along inner margin of eyes; base of each seta tuberculate.

Antennal insertion about 2 torular diameters above clypeal margin; scrobes smooth, not carinate anteriorly. Antennae with scape dark brown, pedicel and funicular segments yellow-brown, and club grading to darker brown at apex; length approximately 2× width; funicle relatively elongate, with F1 longer than broad and only F5 broader than long (Fig. 6); club segmented, 0.5–0.7(0.6)× as long as funicle. Malar groove incomplete, reduced to a shallow remnant; malar space about equal to vertical axis of eye. Genal carina striate. Mandible with a broad, pointed lower tooth and 2 blunt upper teeth.

Thorax shiny black, convex in lateral aspect. Pronotum unsculptured; pronotal ring with about 10 strong, black setae. Mesoscutum and scapulae unsculptured, smooth and shiny; pilosity reduced to a pair of black setae between notauli. Notauli incomplete, in the form of broad, shallow pits, finely and sparsely punctured around circumference (Fig. M1). Scutellum more or less square, convex in lateral aspect, irregularly striate anterior to frenal groove; scutellar setae long and black; frenal area smooth, delimited by an indented groove consisting of a row of punctures. Axillae smooth. Mesepisternal depression striate; mesepimeron smooth, including dimple. Dorsellum longitudinally striate; remainder of metanotum smooth, with furrow finely striate.

Forewing (Fig. 19) hyaline or diffusely pale brown, without a definite infumate patch. Marginal vein 1.8–2.3(2.01)× as long as stigmal vein. Postmarginal vein about 1.2× as long as stigmal vein. Stigmal area with scattered setae. Costal cell not excised at apex, almost entirely margined by setae; ventral row of setae continuous. Submarginal vein with 9–11 setae. Basal hairline faintly pigmented, with a line of about 5 setae; basal cell bare, margined by cubital hairline. Speculum present; linea calva not differentiated.

Coxae dark yellow-brown, not striate; hind coxae with dorsal crest of setae present, lateral setae absent. Hind tibiae with 1 spur, 0.2–0.3× as long as hind basitarsus.

Propodeum shiny black; basal fovea present. Plica absent, but horizontal carinae present posterior to costula. Surface of tooth smooth. Nucha rugose.

Gaster dark brown-black grading to brown at apex, or entirely brown. T1 covering 0.6–0.9× as long as gaster; setae at base long but sparse. Ovipositor projecting slightly from base of gaster. S1 with entire surface finely striate, giving a matt appearance; anterior half with shallow alveolae (Fig. M2).

Male. Head very dark red-brown. Antennal insertions 2.5–3 torular diameters above clypeal margin. Antennae with scape and pedicel brown-black, funicle and club black; F1 the longest funicular segment; club 1.1–1.5(1.25)× as long as F1; funicular setae approximately as long as their segment of origin.

Mesoscutum mostly smooth, but with some transverse rugosity, and with approx. 4 pairs of setae. Notauli defined anteriorly, becoming a groove posteriorly. Scapulae smooth and shiny. Forewing hyaline. Marginal vein 1.7–2.3× as long as stigmal vein (mean 2.05). Setae present along 95% of margin of costal cell. Basal hairline infumate, with a line of about 6 setae; basal cell sparsely setose, margined by cubital hairline. Linea calva narrower than in female. Legs with fore and middle coxae dark brown, hind coxae black. Femora dark brown, yellow towards apex. Tarsi and tibiae yellow-brown to darker brown.

Gaster narrower and more elongate than in female; basal fovea wide and deep.

Type data. Holotype (NZAC): female, "NEW ZEALAND OL/ Kirks Bush/ L. Hawea Jan 1981," "swept/ J. S. Noyes/ E. W. Valentine," "*Nothofagus* For/ Broadleaf/ *P. totara*."

Paratypes (44 females, 12 males; NZAC unless otherwise noted): 1 female, NN, Cobb Rd summit, Asbestos Mine Track, 880 m, 10 Feb 1985, R.M. Emberson, beaten from beech (LUNZ); 3 females, 2 males, NN, Nelson, 8 Mar 1966, DBR, ex *Eriococcus* on *Nothofagus truncata* (1164); 2 females, Upper Takaka R., asbestos mine track, JSN, EWV, AKW, 700 m, 2 Dec 1980, mixed *Nothofagus* forest; 1 female, NN, Cobb Ridge (S), 1100 m, 3 Dec 1980, JSN, EWV, AKW, native tussock grassland; 2 females, NN, Dun Mtn, 2000 ft [600 m], 25 Jan 1931, ESG; 3 females, BR, L. Rotoiti, 600 m, Nov–Dec 1980, F. Dodge, Malaise trap, edge of *Nothofagus* forest; 4 females, BR, St Arnaud, 600 m, 9 Dec 1980, JSN, EWV, AKW, *Nothofagus* forest; 1 female, BR, Lewis Pass, 500 m, 19 Jan 1976, AKW, sweeping in bush and beside road; 1 female, BR, Mt Robert, 600 m, 10 Dec 1980, JSN, EWV, AKW, *Nothofagus* forest and grass; 1 female, BR, Mt Robert, 7 Nov 1971, EWV, swept grasses; 1 female, MC, Pudding Hill Domain, 800 m, 19 Sep 1981, JWE, sweeping in *Nothofagus solandri* forest (LUNZ); 4 females, MC, Mt Hutt, Scotts Saddle, 1000 m, 27 Nov 1981, JWE, *Nothofagus* forest edge (LUNZ); 1 female, MC, Alford Forest, 2 Nov 1960, RJM; 13 females, 7 males (4 females, 2 males in ANIC), same data as holotype; 3 females, 1 male, OL, L. Wakatipu, Bobs Cove, 23 Jan 1981, JSN, EWV, swept, *Nothofagus* forest, mixed broadleaf; 3 females, 1 male, OL, Kinloch S.F., Dart R., Jan 1981, JSN, EWV, swept, *Nothofagus* forest, broadleaf, grass, *P. totara*; 1 male, FD, Fiordland N.P., Grebe Vly, S arm L. Manapouri, 170 m, 4 Jan 1982, JWE, C.A. Muir, P.T. Syrett, sweeping ferns.

Material examined. Type series only.
— / NN, BR, MC, OL, FD.

Biology. The only host recorded is *Eriococcus* sp. on *Nothofagus truncata*.

Remarks. *Aphobetus cultratus* is diagnosed by its groove-like notauli. It is named from the Latin 'cultratus,' knife-shaped, in reference to this feature.

Aphobetus cyanea (Bouček)

Fig. 7, 20, M3–6; Map 2

cyanea Bouček, 1988a: 364, fig. 680, 681 (*Modronila*).
  Valentine & Walker 1991: 28.

Female. Head black with strong metallic blue lustre to dark red with slight purple lustre; dorsal margin weakly concave. Face 1.4–1.6(1.54)× broader than long. Posterior ocelli immediately adjacent to strong occipital carina, not crossing it. Back of head smooth to very finely rugose, margined just below occipital carina with a transverse row of setae. OD approximately 0.35× OOL. Vertex not sculptured, smooth, shiny, with scattered long white setae.

Antennal insertions slightly more than 1 torular diameter above clypeal margin; scrobes not delimited, shallow even towards toruli, not sculptured, not carinate anteriorly. Antennae (Fig. 7) unicolorous mid to dark brown; scape long, slender; pedicel elongate pyriform; F1 to F4 longer than broad, F5 square; setae shorter than their segment of origin; sensilla present; club 0.4–0.6(0.51)× as long as funicle. Genae smooth, with 3 rows of white setae; genal carina moderately wide, not striate. Malar groove represented only by a deep remnant on either side of clypeus; malar space slightly shorter than long axis of eye. Mandible with a broad, pointed lower tooth and 2 pointed upper teeth.

Thorax black with strong metallic blue lustre to dark red-brown with pale purple lustre. Pronotum rugose anteriorly, smooth posteriorly, bearing scattered long setae with base raised; pronotal ring with about 16 setae. Mesoscutum smooth anteriorly, with paired setae to regular long setation, imbricate posteriorly, with 2 pairs of setae. Notauli almost complete, narrow anteriorly and transversely striate, widening to a shallow groove posteriorly (Fig. M3). Scapulae smooth, with a row of long setae beside notauli. Scutellum longer than broad, flat in lateral aspect, engraved reticulate; anterior pair of setae closer together than posterior pair. Frenal area large, delimited by a line consisting of fine, short grooves (Fig. M3). Axillae mainly smooth, with several long setae separated anteriorly from scutellum by a shallow groove, grading into a deep fovea. Mesepisternal depression quadrangular; mesepimeron smooth, shiny, with dimple barely noticeable. Dorsellum striate; fovea and remainder of metanotum smooth.

Forewing (Fig. 20) hyaline. Marginal vein 3.0–5.8 (4.27)× as long as stigmal vein. Stigmal area setose. Postmarginal vein 1.2× as long as stigmal vein. Costal cell excised at apex, marginally setose, with several complete rows of ventral setae. Basal hairline not demarcated, not infumate; basal cell setose, margined by cubital row of setae. Speculum absent; linea calva almost the only bare patch on forewing.

Legs dark orange-brown, darker brown on dorsal surface of femora; coxae metallic. Hind coxae without dorsal or lateral crests of setae, but a sparse ventral line present. Hind tibia with a single spur 0.95× as long as hind basitarsus.

Propodeum dark, with slight metallic blue lustre. Medial tooth (Fig. M4) ending in a half cup, smooth-surfaced, flanked by longitudinal carinae. Nucha broader than long, rugose. Basal fovea, costula, and medial plica present. A large, whitish tuft of setae at spiracle.

Gaster oval, black with strong metallic blue lustre to dark red-brown with faint purple lustre. T1 about 0.8× as long as gaster. S1 not striate (Fig. M5, M6).

Male. Head metallic blue to dark red, with faint metallic lustre. Antennal insertions about 2 torular diameters above clypeal margin. Antennae with funicular segments nodose, decreasing in length from F1 towards apex; setae conspicuous, but shorter than their segment of origin; club 0.9–1.2(1.06)× as long as F1.

Forewing hyaline. Marginal vein 2.8–4.9(3.61)× as long as stigmal. Costal cell entirely margined with setae. Basal hairline not infumate, not demarcated; basal cell less setose than in female; cubital hairline present.

Type data. Holotype (NZAC): female, "617," "NEW ZEALAND (NC)/ Lewis Pass? xii.1962 B. B. Given," ex Eriococcus/ nitidus on/ Poa caespitosa," "Holo/ -type [and underneath] Bck/ 86," "HOLOTYPE/ [f] Modronila/ cyanea g.sp.n./ det Z. Bouček, 1984."

Paratypes (2 females, 2 males; NZAC):1 female, TK, N Egmont, 21 Apr 1946, M.W. Carter, ex Eriococcus on Danthonia; 1 female, OL, Coronet Pk, 1640 m, Jan 1981, tussock/alpine shrubs, Hebe mat plants, swept, JSN, EWV; 1 male, BR, Mt Robert, 15 Mar 1968, EWV, 1521; 1 male, same data as holotype.

Material examined. Type series, plus 74 non-type examples (14 males, 60 females; NZAC, unless otherwise noted). **TK.** N Egmont, 21 Apr 1946, M.W. Carter, ex Eriococcus on Danthonia, 1 female. Pouakai Range, Pouakai Ridge, 1280–1370 m, 1–2 Dec 1975, JSD or AKW, sweeping or Malaise trap, 5 females (1 ANIC). **NN.** Mt Arthur: 25 Feb 1924, A. Philpott, 1 female; 914 m, 2 Jan 1929, ESG, 1 female; 1340 m, 22 Jan 1948, JTS, ex tussock, 1 female. Burgoo Creek, 6 Dec 1960, ex Eriococcus on Chionochloa, FRNZ, 1 male, 3 females. Cobb Ridge S, 1100 m, 3 Dec 1980, JSN, EWV, AKW, native tussock grassland, 4 females (1 ANIC). Cobb Reservoir, 850 m, 6 Dec 1980, Nothofagus forest, JSN, EWV, AKW, 6 females. **NN/MB.** Red Hills, 1370 m, 10 Feb 1964, JSD, ex red narrow-leaved tussock, host ?Eriococcus nitidulus, 1 female. **BR.** Travers Range, Angelus Hut, 1740 m, 5 Feb 1964, JSD, ex Eriococcus [dan]thoniae on Chionochloa, 1 male, 1 female. Mt Robert: 15 Mar 1968, EWV, 1521, 8 males, 11 females (1 female 1 male ANIC); 823 m, nr L Rotoiti, 16 Jan 1976, AKW, beating Nothofagus menziesii with parasitic fungi, 1 female; 1340 m, 16 Jan 1976, AKW, sweeping tussock, 1 female. **WD.** Westland N.P., Castle Rocks v, 1370 m, 15 Jan 1986, JWE, sweeping subalpine tussock, 2 females (LUNZ). **NC.** 20 Dec 1962, BBG, ex Eriococcus nitidulus on Poa caespitosa, 2 males, 1 female. **MC.** Cragieburn Range, Porter Creek, 1220 m, Apr 1969, JSD, beating, 1 female. **CO.** Symes Rd, 1220 m, 7 Feb 1986, C.A. Muir, sweeping tussock, 1 female (LUNZ). **DN.** Table Hill, Hut Creek, 305 m, 16 Feb 1968, JSD, 1 male. **FD.** Fiordland N.P., Murchison Mtns, E McKenzie Burn, 1110 m, 4 Dec 1993, C.A. Muir, sweeping Hebe and tussock scrub, 1 female (LUNZ). Turret Range, half way to Wolfe Flat, 22 Jan 1970, ACE, sweeping, 1 male, 1 female. W Olivine Range, Tempest Spur, 914–1219 m, 25 Jan 1975, GWR, under stones, 1 female. **SI.** Rakeahua Camp, 8 Feb 1968, EWV, 1441, 9 females (2 ANIC).

TK / NN, BR, WD, NC, MC, OL, DN, CO, FD / SI.

Biology. *Aphobetus cyanea* is a primary parasitoid of Eriococcidae in alpine habitats. It has been reared from *Eriococcus* sp. on *Danthonia* and *Chionochloa*; *E. nitidulus* on *Poa caespitosa*, and *E. [?]thoniae* (illegible, probably *danthoniae*) on *Chionochloa*.

Remarks. *A. cyanea* is diagnosed by the forewing having a setose basal cell and a long marginal vein (average 4× as long as stigmal vein), and lacking a speculum. A series of 3 females and 1 male in NZAC (NN, Dun Mtn, 4 Feb 1924, A. Philpott) show slight differences. The body colour is dark red-brown with a slight purple metallic lustre, there are fewer setae between the notauli (5 pairs not 7), and the basal cell in the forewing is slightly less setose. These differences are not sufficient to justify describing another species without further material.

Aphobetus erroli new species

Fig. M7–9; Map 3

Female. Head brown to black, shiny; dorsal margin slightly concave. Face 1.4–1.6(1.48)× broader than long. Occipital carina strong; back of head imbricate. OD about equal to OOL. Vertex long-setose.

Antennal insertions about 2 torular diameters above clypeal margin; scrobes sculptured centrally, smooth laterally, not carinate anteriorly. Antennae with flagellum and pedicel honey yellow, scape darker at base, F1 occasionally darker; funicular segments not compressed, only F5 broader than long; club 0.7–0.8(0.73)× as long as funicle. Malar groove an incomplete remnant above mandibles, inconspicuous, striate; malar space shorter than vertical axis of eye. Genal carina striate. Mandible with a broad, pointed lower tooth and 2 blunter upper teeth.

Thorax shiny black. Pronotal ring with about 10 setae. Mesoscutum transversely rugose between notauli, with paired setae. Notauli incomplete, composed of well defined small pits anteriorly grading to a large, less well defined groove posteriorly (Fig. M7). Scapulae longitudinally striate. Scutellum only slightly broader than long (length about 0.9× width), convex in lateral aspect, engraved reticulate in anterior two-thirds, the sculpture changing at posterior pair of setae to become faintly longitudinally striate; a fine transverse line visible at this point, but no indented frenal groove (Fig. M7, M8). Axillae weakly striate. Depression in mesepisternum striate around edges, smooth centrally; mesepimeron glabrous, with a striate dimple. Dorsellum striate; remainder of metanotum finely striate; furrow smooth.

Forewing with a faint to dark infumate patch posterior to marginal and stigmal veins, fading out towards posterior margin. Wing hyaline proximally and in distal quarter to fifth. Marginal vein 1.8–2.4(2.07)× as long as stigmal vein. Postmarginal vein 1.1–1.2× as long as stigmal vein. Stigmal area devoid of setae. Costal cell not excised at apex, with setae along distal 75% of margin; ventral row of setae continuous. Submarginal vein with 6–8 setae. Basal hairline faintly pigmented, with about 4 setae; basal cell bare, margined by cubital hairline. Speculum present; linea calva not differentiated.

Legs brown-yellow; coxae brown. Hind coxae without dorsal or lateral crests of setae. Hind tibial spur present, half as long as short hind basitarsus.

Propodeum dark brown-black; basal fovea present (Fig. M8). Plica complete; an additional medial plica present posteriorly only. Tooth smooth, slightly striate. Nucha with an apical fovea, transversely rugose.

Gaster rectangular, from pale brown basally and dark brown apically to entirely dark brown. T1 0.95× as long as gaster; setae at base sparse. Ovipositor slightly extended past end of gaster. S1 finely striate, matt in appearance; a smooth medial ridge separating 2 large anterior alveolae from 4 wide posterior alveolae (Fig. M9).

Male. Head very dark red-brown. Antennal insertions 2.5–3 torular diameters above clypeal margin. Antennae with F1 the longest funicular segment; club 1.1–1.5(1.28)× as long as funicle; flagellar setae relatively short, about as long as segment of origin.

Forewing with infumate patch paler and less extensive than in female. Marginal vein 1.8–2.4(2.18)× as long as stigmal vein. Distal 60% of costal cell margined with setae. Basal hairline faintly pigmented, with about 8 setae; basal cell sparsely setose, margined by cubital hairline.

Type data. Holotype (NZAC): female, "NEW ZEALAND WN/ Bal[l]ance Bridge/ Res. 3 Jan 1975," "J. C. Watt/ litter 75/25."

Paratypes (13 females, 5 males; NZAC, unless otherwise noted): 1 female, TO, Omoho Stream, 27 Mar 1969, HAO, Malaise; 3 females, NN, Lower Moutere, one 24 Jul 1964 on *Coprosma repens*, two 30 Jul 1964 on lemonwood in assoc. with *Ctenochiton*, DBR; 7 females (1 ANIC), 1 male, NN, Nelson, 13 Jan 1965, EWV, *Ctenochiton perforatus* on *Pittosporum eugenioides* (719); 2 females, 2 males, NN, Nelson, Feb 1962, EWV, on *Rhododendron*; 1 male, NN, Nelson, 28 Jan 1965, EWV, ex *Ctenochiton perforatus* on *Pittosporum eugenioides* (719) (ANIC).

Material examined. Type series only.
TO, WN / NN.

Biology. Reared from *Ctenochiton perforatus* on *Pittosporum eugenioides*, and from *Ctenochiton* sp.

Remarks. *Aphobetus erroli* is diagnosed by the lack of an indented frenal groove, and the forewing being infumate centrally but hyaline proximally and distally. It is named for Mr Errol Valentine, who provided much of the reared material in the NZAC.

Aphobetus maskelli Howard

Fig. 8, 9, M10; Map 4

maskelli Howard, 1896: 166–167 (*Aphobetus*). Ashmead 1904: 328. Valentine 1967: 1127. Bouček 1988a: 363. Valentine & Walker 1991: 28.

Female. Head shiny, brown to black, finely reticulate behind; dorsal margin slightly concave. Face 1.3–1.6 (1.43)× broader than long. Occipital carina strong. Ocelli clear; OD 0.5–0.7× OOL. Setae on vertex long, brown.

Antennal insertions 2 torular diameters above clypeal margin; scrobes finely striate centrally only, not carinate anteriorly. Antennae (Fig. 8) ranging from yellow, with F1 and sometimes F2, F3, and tip or entire club darker, to unicolorous medium brown; F1 longer than broad to square; only F5 broader than long; club 0.5–0.9(0.68)× as long as funicle. Malar groove a conspicuous though incomplete remnant; malar space shorter than vertical axis of eye. Genal carina striate. Mandible with a broad, pointed lower tooth and 2 blunt upper teeth.

Thorax shiny black. Pronotum sculptured anterior to setal ring; ring with about 10 yellow-brown setae visible in dorsal view. Mesoscutum finely reticulate to finely transversely rugose, with 3 or 4 pairs of yellow-brown setae between notauli. Notauli almost complete, consisting of series of small, well defined pits. Scapulae finely longitudinally striate to smooth. Scutellum convex in lateral aspect, square to slightly longer than broad, engraved reticulate anterior to frenal groove; frenal area almost smooth to finely longitudinally striate, delimited by indented frenal groove consisting of a row of punctures. Axillae almost smooth. Depression in mesepisternum striate; upper and lower mesepimeron glabrous, without a dimple. Dorsellum, remainder of metanotum, and furrow striate.

Propodeum dark brownish-black; basal fovea present. Plica complete, without additional plicae. Tooth smooth, delimited by longitudinal carinae. Nucha matt, long.

Forewing with infumate patch faint and diffuse to strong and compact. Marginal vein 1.5–2.7(1.85)× as long as stigmal vein. Postmarginal vein subequal in length to stigmal vein. Stigmal area devoid of setae. Costal cell not excised at apex; margined with setae along distal 75% of length; ventral row of setae continuous. Submarginal vein with 10–15 setae. Basal hairline infumate, with 5 or 6 setae; basal cell bare, margined by cubital row of setae. Speculum wide; linea calva not differentiated.

Fore and middle coxae yellow-brown to dark brown; hind coxae dark brown, with a dorsal crest of setae only. Femora grading from dark brownish-yellow basally to yellow-brown apically. Tibiae yellow-brown; hind tibial spur approximately as long as basitarsus, but darker. Tarsal segments yellow, darkening towards apex.

Gaster dark brown, paler at base and apex. T1 extending 0.6–0.9× length of gaster; setae at base sparse. Ovipositor exserted beyond last tergite. S1 finely striate, slightly concave anteriorly, with a smooth, non-striate horizontal ridge medially and 4 large alveolae posteriorly (Fig. M10).

Male. Head dark brown-black, with vertex very finely rugose. Antennal insertions 2.5–3 torular diameters above clypeal margin. Antennae (Fig. 9) dark brown, with scape and pedicel sometimes paler; F1 the longest funicular segment; club 1.2–1.7(1.47)× as long as F1.

Forewing with a very faint infumate patch. Marginal vein 1.6–2.3(1.92)× as long as stigmal vein. Costal cell margined with setae along distal 70%. Basal hairline infumate, with a line of about 6 setae; basal cell sparsely setose, margined by cubital hairline. Speculum absent, but sparse setae present posterior to submarginal and marginal veins. Hind tibial spur concolorous with basitarsus.

Type data. Since a holotype was not designated by Howard—"One female, four males, reared by W.M. Maskell, New Zealand, from *Ctenochiton viridis*"—his specimens are syntypes.

Lectotype (USNM): female, here designated, "from/ Maskell./ N. Zealand," "Par: on/ *Ctenochiton*/ *viridis*," "Type No./ 26030/ U.S.N.M.," "*Aphobetus*/ *maskelli* How./ type [f]".

Paralectotypes (3 males, USNM, BMNH): 2 (USNM), same data as lectotype but one with added "Paratype" label and one with added "Allotype" and "*Aphobetus maskelli* How./ type [m];" 1 (BMNH), same data as lectotype but with added (modern) "Para-/ type" and " [m] *Aphobetus*/ *maskelli* Ashm./ PT, det. Bck. 76."

Material examined. Type series, plus 290 non-type examples (240 females, 49 males; NZAC, unless otherwise noted). **ND**. Waipoua Kauri Forest, 11–12 Dec 1983, L. Masner, 2 females (ANIC). Omahuta S.F., 6 Oct 1980, JSN, 1 female. **AK**. Waitakere Range, JSN, 28 females (5 ANIC): Aug 1980 (1), Sep 1980 (5), Oct 1980 (7), Nov 1980 (6), Dec 1980 (4), Jan 1981 (5). Titirangi, Malaise trap in garden, Oct 1980 (2), Nov 1980 (1), GWR, 3 females. Kauri Park, 23 Oct 1980, JSN, 1 female. Lynfield, GK, 3 females: 7 Dec 1974, 12 Feb 1975, Nov 1980. Takapuna, 18 Apr 1966, ex *Nipaecoccus aurilanatus* on *Araucaria excelsa* (1208), PSC, 15 females, 4 males. Whatipu, 24–25 Feb 1979: on *Ulex* foliage, AKW, 1 female; LAM, 2 females. **CL**. Little Barrier I., 183 m, 21 Feb 1976, AKW, sweeping, 1 female. 19 km E of Tapu, 31 Jan 1981, JSN, 6 females. Kaueranga Vly, 1 Feb 1981, JSN, 2 females. **TK**. Waitaanga Plateau, 14–15 Dec 1983, L. Masner, 1 female (ANIC). **WN**. Waikanae, 4 Oct 1980, CFB, ex *Leucaspis* sp. on *Podocarpus totara,* 1 female. Island Bay, 30 Mar 1931, ESG, 1 female. Days Bay, 8 May 1927, ESG, 1 female. Orongorongo, 25 Jan 1961, RGO, ex fallen white rata (*Metrosideros robusta*), 1 female. **SD**. Stephens I., 14–28 Jan 1933, ESG, 1 female. Pelorus Bridge: Feb 1962, EWV, ex *Ctenochiton viridis* on *Nothopanax arboreum,* 1 female, 1 male; 12 Feb 1963, DBR, ex encyrtid on *Ctenochiton viridis* mature female on *Nothopanax arboreum,* 2 females, 3 males; 14 Mar 1966, DV8, 1 female. **NN**. Eves Valley, 8 Dec 1980, JSN, EWV, AKW, *Podocarpus* forest, 11 females. Totaranui, 600 m, 5 Dec 1980, JSN, EWV, AKW, mixed *Podocarpus* forest, 1 female. Upper Takaka R., asbestos mine track, 700 m, 2 Dec 1980, JSN, EWV, AKW, mixed *Nothofagus* forest, 4 females. Pokororo, 17 Jan 1964, EWV, on *Podocarpus totara,* 1 female. Farewell Spit, 4 Dec 1980, JSN, EWV, AKW, under *Leptospermum,* 2 females.Canaan Saddle, 7 Dec 1980, JSN, EWV, AKW, *Nothofagus*/mixed *Podocarpus,* 2 females, 1 male. Cobb Reservoir, 850 m, 6 Dec 1980, JSN, EWV, AKW, *Nothofagus* forest, 2 females. Whangamoa Saddle, 13 Dec 1980, JSN, EWV, AKW, *Nothofagus*/mixed *Podocarpus,* 1 female. Whangamoa, Nov 1964, EWV, ex ?encyrtid pupa on immature male *Ctenochiton viridis* on *Griselinia littoralis* (909), 1 male. Mt Arthur, 4 Feb 1965, GK, *Nothofagus menziesii* (998), 1 female. Kaihoka Lakes: 12 Jan 1966, AKW, 1 female; 1 Feb 1979, AKW, LAM, *Phormium tenax,* 1 female; 4 Dec 1980, coastal forest, JSN, EWV, AKW, 11 females. Nelson, ESG, 8 females, 6 males: 8 Sep 1926 (1 female), 5 Dec 1926 (3 females, 5 males) 19 Mar 1927 (1 female), 9 Apr 1927 (1 female), 8 Jun 1927 (1 female, 1 male), 22 Jun 1926 (1 female). Nelson, 28 Nov 1960, EWV, on totara (205), 2 males. Nelson, 1 May 1964, EWV, ex *Leucaspis* sp. on totara (756), 1 female. Nelson, 22 Dec 1964, EWV, on totara (921), 1 male. Kaiteriteri, DBR: 1 Feb 1965, *Ctenochiton viridis* on *Nothopanax arboreum* (993), 2 females, 4 males; 4 Feb 1965, ex encyrtid on *Ctenochiton viridis* mature females on *Nothopanax arboreum* (993), 1 female; 13 Feb 1965, ex chermid larva, *Nothopanax arboreum* (994), 1 male. Richmond, 1 Mar 1961, DBR (318), 4 females, 1 male. Ruby

Bay: 18 Nov 1964, EWV, swept native plants (558), 1 female; Jan 1965, EEC, ex aphid! apterous females on mahoe (*Melicytus ramiflora*) (958), 1 female, 3 males. Dun Mtn, 1070 m, 13 Feb 1961 GK, leafmould, 1 female. West Haven Inlet, 27 Jan 1966, JAdB, ex *Ctenochiton viridis* on *Hedycarya arborea* (1138), 3 females, 1 male. Marsden Vly: 26 Nov 1962, EWV, ex *Eriococcus* on *Hedycarya arborea,* 1 female; ex encyrtids ex *Ctenochiton viridis* ovipositing females on *Hedycarya arborea,* BBG, 12 females, 5 males – 3 Dec 1963 (1 male), 22 Jan 1964 (1 female, 1 male), 24 Jan 1964 (7 females, 2 males), 13 Mar 1964 (4 females, 1 male) (716). Punakaiki, 23 Jan 1962, EWV, ex *Ctenochiton* sp., 1 female, 1 male. **MB**. Awatere Vly, 22 Dec 1965, BBG, secondary on *Coccophagus* in *Eriococcus* sp. on *Hebe raoulii* (1111), 2 females, 2 males. E. Wairau Vly, Red Hills, 14 Oct 1964, DBR, ?secondary on ?*Ctenochiton viridis* immature on *Phormium tenax,* 1 female. Wairau, 1070 m, 23 Mar 1972, JAdB, 4 females. **BR**. St Arnaud, 600 m, 9 Dec 1980, native grassland, *Sphagnum* bog, JSN, EWV, AKW, 4 females. L. Rotoiti, 4–9 Feb 1978, S&JP, Malaise by forest stream, 1 male. L. Rotoroa, 11 Dec 1980, JSN, EWV, AKW, 9 females. Buller R., Gowan Bridge, 3 Mar 1969, JAdB, ex ?*Inglisia leptospermi* on *Leptospermum ericoides,* 2 females. Maruia Saddle, 457 m, 6 Feb 1977, AKW, on *Rubus* leaves, 1 female. **MC**. W of Staveley, SH 72, 2 Dec 1977 ES, *Nothofagus* forest, 1 female. Riccarton, 12 Jun 1922, 5 females, 1 male. Riccarton Bush, ESG, 34 females: 4 Apr 1921 (1), 18 May 1923 (2), 26 Jun –18 Aug 1920 (7), 11 Aug 1921 (8), Sep 1921 (7), 6 Oct 1920 (6), Oct 1921 (3). Canterbury College, Oct 1921, ESG, 1 female. Redcliffs, Nov 1922, ESG, *Ctenochiton viridis* on *Rubus australis,* 3 females, 1 male. Governors Bay, 1 Jan 1924, ESG, 1 female. Dallington, ESG, 4 females: 8 Jan 1923 (1); 18 Jan 1924 (3). Banks Peninsula, Mt Fitzgerald, 457 m, 24 Jan 1922, ESG, 1 female. **OL**. L. Hawea, Kirks Bush, Jan 1981, swept *Nothofagus* forest, broadleaf, *P. totara,* JSN, EWV, 3 females, 1 male. Kinloch S.F., Dart R., Jan 1981, swept *Nothofagus* forest, broadleaf, grass, *P. totara,* JSN, EWV, 3 females. Mt Aspiring N.P., Makarora, 25 Jan 1981, swept *Nothofagus, Podocarpus,* broadleaf, JSN, EWV, 3 females. L. Wakatipu, Bobs Cove, 23 Jan 1981, swept, *Nothofagus* forest, mixed broadleaf, JSN, EWV, 1 female. Coronet Peak, 1640 m, Jan 1981, swept tussock/alpine shrubs, *Hebe* mat plants, JSN, EWV, 6 females, 1 male. **CO**. Cromwell Gorge, 12–21 Nov 1974, JCW, pit trap, 1 male. Old Man Range, 1340 m, 11 Feb 1982, CFB, sweeping tussock, 1 male (ANIC). Kawerau Gorge, 488 m, 20 Mar 1975, JCW, Malaise trap, 1 female. **FD**. Fiordland N.P., Murchison Mtns, Plateau Creek, 1–3 Dec 1980, R.M. Emberson, Malaise at edge of *Nothofagus menziesii* forest, 1 female (LUNZ). **SL**. Invercargill, Jan 1961, EWV,

?*Ctenochiton* sp. on *Wintera colorata* (234), 4 males (2 ANIC). **SI.** Leasks Bay, 27 Feb 1962, EWV, ex *Powellia* sp. on *Nothopanax arboreum* (458), 1 male. Mason Bay, 26 Feb 1968, EWV (1501), 2 females.

ND, AK, CL, TK, WN / SD, NN, MB, BR, MC, OL, CO, FD, SL, SI.

Biology. *Aphobetus maskelli* has been recorded from *Nipaecoccus aurilanatus, Leucaspis* sp., *Ctenochiton viridis, Eriococcus* sp., ?*Inglisia leptospermi, Powellia* sp., apterous aphids, and a chermid larva. It has also been recorded as a hyperparasitoid through a possible encyrtid larva on *Ctenochiton viridis* and through *Coccophagus* sp. in *Eriococcus* sp.

Remarks. *Aphobetus maskelli* is diagnosed by the combination of a long hind tibial spur and the number of setae on the pronotum (about 10) and submarginal vein (at least 10). It shows far more variability than *A. paucisetosus, A. cultratus,* or *A. erroli,* but there is much more material available. Series show little variation in size or colour, but these features grade from the smallest, darkest specimens to the largest, most colourful ones, and no morphological feature is sufficiently disparate to justify recognising more than one species.

Aphobetus nana (Bouček)

Fig. 21, M12, M13; Map 5

nana Bouček, 1988a: 362, fig. 672–674 (*Pidinka*). Valentine & Walker 1991: 28.

Female. Head brown to black, shiny; dorsal margin moderately concave. Face 1.4–1.8(1.64)× broader than long. Occipital carina moderately strong; back of head smooth centrally, striate laterally. Ocelli clear to reddish; OD less than OOL. Frons with a green tinge, unsculptured, with sparse setae. Vertex moderately long, transversely reticulate between ocelli, also with sparse setae. Antennal insertions slightly less than 2 torular diameters above clypeal margin; scrobes shallow, not defined, but with a narrow, transversely striate groove in the centre, not carinate anteriorly. Antennae honey yellow with darker scapes to unicolorous brown; funicular segments compressed, broader than long except for F1, which is square; club 0.75–0.9(0.84)× as long as funicle. Malar groove incomplete, reduced to a small striate remnant above mandibles; malar space shorter than vertical axis of eye. Lower face convex, with a transverse groove parallel to mouth margin. Genal carina striate. Mandible with a pointed lower tooth and a broad, blunt, undivided upper tooth.

Thorax shiny brown to black, often with a distinct metallic blue tinge. Pronotal ring with about 6 setae. Mesoscutum transversely striate anteriorly, reticulate to longitudinally striate posteriorly, with paired setae. Notauli complete, composed of series of small, well defined pits. Scapulae finely longitudinally striate, grading to reticulate adjacent to notauli. Scutellum 0.8× broader than long, flat in lateral aspect, engraved reticulate over entire surface. Frenal area not delimited by a groove or line, only by a slight change in sculpture (Fig. M12). Axillae sculptured. Mesepisternum with a depressed, finely striate, elongate triangular area. Lower mesepimeron with a shallow, inconspicuous striate dimple. Dorsellum short, triangular, with converging longitudinal striae; remainder of metanotum smooth; metanotal furrow smooth, declivous.

Forewing (Fig. 21) infumate from base, hyaline in distal fifth. Marginal vein 1.7–2.3(2.02)× as long as stigmal vein. Postmarginal vein 1.2× as long as stigmal vein. Stigmal area bare. Costal cell strongly excised at apex, margined with setae along distal 60%; ventral row of setae continuous. Basal hairline pigmented, with several setae; basal cell with 1 or 2 setae, margined by ventral cubital hairline. Speculum present; linea calva not differentiated.

Coxae brown; femora brown apically, sometimes entirely; tibiae sometimes apically brown, basally yellow; tarsi yellow. Fore and hind femora slightly thickened. Hind coxae slightly striate; dorsal and lateral setal crests present. Hind tibial spur 0.8× as long as short hind basitarsus.

Propodeum black, with a basal fovea (Fig. M13). Plica complete, forming a tooth with costula. Tooth shallow, anteriorly smooth, posteriorly delimited by converging longitudinal carinae. Lateral pilosity sparse but fairly long.

Gaster yellow or red-brown basally grading to dark brown to black apically, broad and short, almost square, dorsally somewhat collapsing. T1 usually covering more than 75% of length of gaster. Pilosity at base reduced to several setae. Ovipositor slightly exserted. S1 finely striate except for smooth anterior collar, anteriorly with small alveolae, posteriorly with larger alveolae, these separated by a raised, striate median area.

Male. Head dark orange-brown. Frons with striate indentation, more conspicuous than in female. Antennal insertions 2.5–3 torular diameters above clypeal margin. Antennae with scape and pedicel yellow, funicle brown, club brown, sometimes paler apically; funicular segments more or less equal in length, with F1 only slightly the longer; club 1.4–2.5(1.82)× as long as F1; flagellar setae long, approximately 1.5× as long as segment of origin.

Forewing with an infumate patch, much smaller and paler than in female, only very faintly infumate proximally. Marginal vein 1.8–2.2(2.05)× as long as stigmal vein.

Costal cell margined with setae along distal 60%, slightly excised at apex. Basal hairline faintly pigmented, comprising about 6 setae; basal cell sparsely setose, margined by cubital hairline.

Gaster less broad and basal fovea less shallow than in female. T1 about 0.9× as long as entire gaster.

Type data. Holotype (NZAC): female, "869/2/ [f]," "NEW ZEALAND/ Stoke NN/ 9.x.65 D. B. Read," "*Ctenochiton/ perforatus/* on *Pittosporum/ eugenioides*," "N.Z.Arthropod/ Collection NZAC/ Entomology Div./ DSIR, Auckland/ New Zealand," "Holo-/type [and on underside] Bouček/ 1986," "HOLOTYPE/ [f] *Pidinka/ nana* g.sp.n./ det. Z. Bouček 1986."

Paratypes (95 females, 12 males; NZAC, unless otherwise noted): 3 females, ND, Waipoua Kauri Forest, 11–12 Dec 1983, L. Masner (ANIC); 1 female, ND, Omahuta S.F., 6 Oct 1980, JSN; 8 females, ND, Whangaroa, 12 Sep 1968, RAC, ex *Ctenochiton* sp. on *Corynocarpus laevigata*; 2 females, AK, Waitakere, 20 Sep 1980, EWV; 25 females (4 ANIC), 1 male, AK, Waitakere Range, Aug 1980 (7 females, male), Sep 1980 (12), Oct 1980 (1), Nov 1980 (4), Dec 1980 (1), JSN; 1 female, AK, Laingholm, Oct 1980, RK, Malaise trap in native bush; 1 female, AK, Lynfield, Wattle Bay, Apr 1980, GK; 2 females, AK, Titirangi, Aug–Sep 1980, PAM, Malaise trap in garden (1); 2 females, AK, Titirangi, Oct 1980, GWR, Malaise trap in garden; 1 female, AK, Huia, May 1975, Malaise; 1 female, AK, Huia, Oct 1980, BMM, Malaise trap in bush; 1 female, AK, Huia Dam, 26 Sep – 10 Oct 1980, ex coccid on *Aristotelia serrata*, GH; 3 females, Birkenhead, Oct 1980 (1), Nov 1980 (2), JFL, Malaise trap in second growth bush; 3 females, SD, Q. Charlotte Sd, Mistletoe Bay, 13 Feb 1985, JWE, sweeping ferns in coastal forest (LUNZ); 1 female, SD, Pelorus Bridge, 8 Nov 1962, EWV, swept, short growth under beech; 3 females, SD, Pelorus Bridge, 14 Mar 1966, DV8; 5 females, SD, Pelorus Bridge, 13 Dec 1980, JSN, EWV, AKW, *Podocarpus* forest; 1 female, NN, Farewell Spit, 4 Dec 1980, JSN, EWV, AKW, under *Leptospermum*; 1 female, NN, Canaan Saddle, 7 Dec 1980, JSN, EWV, AKW, *Nothofagus*/mixed *Podocarpus*; 5 females, NN, Kaihoka Lakes, 4 Dec 1980, JSN, EWV, AKW, coastal forest; 4 females, NN, Totaranui, 600 m, 5 Dec 1980, JSN, EWV, AKW, mixed *Podocarpus* forest; 4 females, NN, upper Takaka R., asbestos mine track, 700 m, 2 Dec 1980, JSN, EWV, AKW, mixed *Nothofagus* forest; 2 males, NN, Mt Cobb, 2 Nov 1960, ex *Ctenochiton* on *Griselinea littoralis* (FR4); 2 males, NN, Eves Vly, 16 Dec 1963, DH, ex *Ctenochiton* male on *Nothopanax arboreum* (710); 1 male, NN, Eves Vly, 10 Nov 1964, DH, ex *Ctenochiton viridis* immature male on *Nothopanax arboreum* (900); 1 male, NN, Maitai, 4 Nov 1963, ESG,

Ctenochiton male (702) on broadleaf; 4 females, NN, Whangamoa, 26 Oct 1962, EWV, ex *Ctenochiton* on *Griselinia littoralis* (573); 3 females, NN, Whangamoa, 20 Nov 1964, EWV, ex *Ctenochiton viridis* immature males on *Griselinia littoralis* (910); 1 female, NN, Whangamoa Saddle, 27 Jan – 3 Feb 1979, AKW, LAM, *Nothofagus* forest; 1 female, NN, Whangamoa Saddle, 27 Jan 1979, LAM; 2 females, NN, Whangamoa Saddle, 13 Dec 1980, JSN, EWV, AKW, *Nothofagus*/mixed *Podocarpus* forest; 3 females, 1 male, NN, Nelson, 7 Sep 1964 (1 female, ex *Ctenochiton ?perforatus* immature males on *Coprosma robusta*), 12 Sep 1964 (1 female, ex *Ctenochiton perforatus* immature male on *Coprosma robusta*), 5 Oct 1964 (1 female, ex *Ctenochiton perforatus* on *Pittosporum eugenioides*), 6 Oct 1964 (male, ex *Ctenochiton ?perforatus* immature male on *Pittosporum eugenioides*), JAdB; 1 female, NN, Dun Mtn, Third House, 29 Jan 1979, AKW, recently fallen *Nothofagus fusca*; 1 female, 2 males, NN, Stoke, 9 Oct 1965, DBR, *Ctenochiton perforatus* on *Pittosporum eugenioides* (869); 1 female, 2 males, NN, Cawthron Institute Gardens, 30 Oct 1967, EWV, *Ctenochiton* on *P. eugenioides*; 5 females, SL, Invercargill, Jan 1961, EWV, ex *?Ctenochiton* sp. on *Wintera colorata* (234).

Material examined. Type series, plus 64 non-type examples (55 females, 3 males, NZAC; 5 females, 1 male, ANIC).

ND, AK, CL, BP, GB, TK, TO, WN / SD, NN, MC, MK, CO, OL, SL / SI.

Biology. Hosts of *A. nana* include *Ctenochiton* sp., *C. viridis*, *C. perforatus*, and *C. elaeocarpi* on *Elaeocarpus hookerianus*; *Pseudococcus longispinus* on *Lawsoniana* hedge; and *Leucaspis mixta*. One record reads "from *Ctenochiton pilporus* [sic] on *Dysoxylum spectabile*;" presumably this is a misspelling of *C. piperis*.

Remarks. *Aphobetus nana* is diagnosed by the flattened scutellum lacking differentiation of a frenum, compressed funicular segments in the female antennae, and strong excision at the apex of the forewing costal cell.

Aphobetus paucisetosus new species

Fig. 1, 10, 11, M14, M15; Map 6

Female (Fig 1). Head shiny black; dorsal margin slightly concave. Face 1.4–1.7(1.5)× broader than long. Occipital carina strong; back of head finely reticulate laterally, imbricate centrally. Ocelli clear to red; OD 0.5× OOL.

Setae on vertex long, brown, those on frons reduced, not conspicuously tuberculate at base.

Antennal insertions about 1.5 torular diameters above clypeal margin; scrobes striate centrally, not carinate anteriorly. Antennae (Fig. 10) from yellow-brown with darker scape and pedicel to unicolorous brown; F1 broader than long to square; F2 slightly broader than long; F3 to F5 square; club $0.7–0.9(0.82)\times$ as long as funicle. Malar groove absent, its remnant inconspicuous; malar space shorter than vertical axis of eye. Genal carina striate (Fig. M14). Mandible with a pointed lower tooth and 2 blunt upper teeth.

Thorax dark brown to black. Pronotal ring setae reduced to 4. Mesoscutum finely reticulate, with 2 pairs of setae between notauli. Notauli a complete, well defined series of regular pits extending to scutellum. Scapulae finely reticulate. Scutellum from square to slightly longer than wide, convex in lateral aspect, anteriorly reticulate; frenal area less sculptured, delimited by indented frenal groove consisting of a row of punctures. Axillae sculptured. Mesepisternum and lower mesepimeron finely striate (Fig. M14), only upper mesepinotum glabrous; dimple absent. Dorsellum striate; remainder of metanotum matt and very thin, with furrow smooth.

Forewing with a darkly infumate patch extending from basal line to end of stigmal vein. Marginal vein 2–2.7 $(2.25)\times$ as long as stigmal vein. Postmarginal vein 1.1–1.2× as long as stigmal vein. Stigmal area bare. Costal cell inconspicuously excised at apex, with distal 75% of margin setose; ventral row of setae continuous. Submarginal vein with reduced number of setae (about 5). Basal hairline absent or with up to 2 setae; basal cell bare, infumate; cubital line of setae absent. Speculum present; linea calva not differentiated. Setae on distal half of forewing sparse.

Legs yellow-brown, more yellow apically on femora and tibiae; coxae dark yellow-brown, slightly striate; tarsi paler. Setal crests absent from hind coxae. Hind tibial spur subequal in length to hind basitarsus.

Propodeum dark brown to black, with a basal fovea present; plicae absent; tooth smooth anteriorly, matt posteriorly; nucha matt.

Gaster dark yellow-brown to dark brown. Setae at base numerous, but not forming a compact tuft. T1 extending 0.8–0.9× length of gaster. Ovipositor projecting slightly from end of gaster. S1 finely striate, the striae interrupted and confused medially in a raised band, with an impressed line anteriorly and 2 vague foveae posteriorly (Fig. M15).

Male. Head dark red-brown. Antennal insertions 2.5–3 torular diameters above clypeal margin. Antennae (Fig. 11) with scape and pedicel dark yellow-brown, funicular segments dark brown, and club paler; F1 subequal in length to F2; club 1.5–2(1.79)× as long as F1; funicular setae long, approximately twice as long as segment of origin.

Forewing with infumate patch varying from pale to dark. Marginal vein 1.7–2.4(2.02)× as long as stigmal vein. Costal cell margined with setae along distal 70%. Basal hairline infumate, with 2 setae; basal cell sparsely setose, margined by cubital hairline. Coxae, femora, and tibiae dark yellow-brown, paler apically (in some specimens quite markedly); tarsi yellow, grading to dark claws.

Gaster rich brown anteriorly grading to dark brown posteriorly, or entirely dark brown.

Type data. Holotype (NZAC): female, "NEW ZEALAND BR/ Lake Rotoroa/ 11 Dec 1980," "J. S. Noyes/ E. W. Valentine/ A. K. Walker."

Paratypes (118 females, 17 males; NZAC, unless otherwise noted): 1 male, Three Kings Is, Great I., 28–30 Nov 1983, CFB, on *Myoporum laetum*. 1 female, ND, Poor Knights Is, Tawhiti Rahi, N Track, Dec 1980, MFT, sweeping; 1 female, ND, Poor Knights Is, Tawhiti Rahi, Plateau, 8 Dec 1980, JCW, beaten at night; 1 female, AK, Waitakere, 20 Sep 1980, EWV; 21 females, 2 males (6 + 1 ANIC), AK, Waitakere Range, JSN, Aug 1980 (1 female), Sep 1980 (11 females), Oct 1980 (7 females), Nov 1980 (2 females, 2 males); 1 female, AK, Titirangi, Aug 1980; **??**, AK, Kauri Park, 23 Aug 1980, JSN; 2 females, AK, Birkenhead, JFL, Sep and Nov 1980, Malaise trap in second growth bush; 1 female, AK, Huia, Sep 1974, BMM, kauri/manuka, Malaise; 1 male, AK, Huia, 29 Aug – 29 Sep 1980, CFB, ex *Leucaspis* on *Cyathodes fasciculatum* (80/ 247H); 2 males, AK, Huia, 12 Sep – 10 Oct 1980, CFB, ex eriococcid on *Cyathodes fasciculatum* (80/247I); 7 females, AK, Lynfield, 3 Aug 1980 (2), 10 Aug 1980 (1), 31 Aug 1980 (2), Sep 1980 (1), Oct 1980 (1), GK; 4 females, CL, 19 km E of Tapu, 31 Jan 1981, JSN; 5 females, CL, Kaueranga Vly, 1 Feb 1981, JSN; 2 females, 2 males, CL, Waiomu Bay, 23 Oct 1968, RAC, from *Phyllocladus trichomanoides*; 1 female, CL, Ohena I., 25–27 Nov 1972, GWR, on *Coprosma melicytus*; 1 female, CL, Ohena I., Old Man Rock, 26 Nov 1972, DM, litter 72/240; 6 females, 3 males, CL, Ruamahuanui I., GWR, 10 Nov 1972 on *Pittosporum* (3 females, 1 male), 12 Nov 1972 litter 72/202 (1 male), 8–12 Nov 1972 (1 female), 14 Nov 1972 litter 72/204 (1 female, 1 male), 14 Nov 1972 litter 72/203 (1 female); 1 female, TO, 20 miles [32 km] SE of Taupo, 20 Feb 1979, LAM; 1 female, TK, Mt Egmont, Holly Hut, 950 m, 28 Nov 1975, AKW, beating; 1 female, WN, Tararua Range, Dundas Hut Ridge, 4 Feb 1985, BAH, beating; 2 males, Stokes Vly, 30 Dec 1958, BAH, beaten (DM250); 1 male, SD, Stephens I., 14–28 Jan 1933, ESG; 1 female, SD, Pelorus Bridge, 19 Feb 1962, DBR, on *Myrtus bullata*; 1 female, SD, Pelorus Bridge, 19 Sep 1968, EWV, ex

Eriococcus on *Cyathodes*; 3 females, SD, Pelorus Bridge, 13 Dec 1980, JSN, EWV, AKW, *Podocarpus* forest; 22 females, NN, Nelson, 22 Jun 1926 (14), 10 Oct 1926 (2), 11 Dec 1926 (3) 19 Mar 1927 (2), 8 Jun 1927 (1), ESG; 1 female, NN, Nelson, 10 Sep 1964, DBR, on *Pittosporum tenuifolium*; 1 female, NN, Nelson, 16 Aug 1971, JAdB, ex "*Eriococcus hookerianus*;" 1 female, NN, Ruby Bay, 19 Feb 1964, EWV, *Eriococcus* past maturity, ngaio (726); 2 females, NN, Ruby Bay, 14 Dec 1964, DBR, ex *Eriococcus* eggsac, mahoe (924); 2 females, NN, Ruby Bay, 18 Nov 1964, EWV, swept from native plants (558); 1 female, NN, Ruby Bay, 3 Dec 1969, JAdB, ex *Eriococcus* on *Loranthus*; 6 females, NN, Totaranui, 600 m, 5 Dec 1980, JSN, EWV, AKW, mixed *Podocarpus* forest; 1 female, NN, Karamea, Kongahu, Nov 1980, P. Quinn, Malaise trap; 2 females, NN, Eves Vly, 8 Dec 1980, JSN, EWV, AKW, *Podocarpus* forest; 2 females, NN, upper Takaka R., asbestos mine track, 700 m, 2 Dec 1980, JSN, EWV, AKW, mixed *Nothofagus* forest; 1 female, NN, Roding R., 19 Oct 1965, JIT; 1 male, NN, Kaihoka Lakes, 4 Dec 1980, coastal forest, JSN, EWV, AKW; 1 male, NN, Aniseed Vly, 21 Jan 1969, JAdB, ex *Eriococcus* on *Myrtus obcordata*; 1 male, NN, Whangamoa Saddle, 27 Jan 1979, LAM; 4 females, NN, L. Rotoroa, 11 Dec 1980, JSN, EWV, AKW, *Podocarpus* forest; 2 females, NN, St Arnaud, 600 m, 9 Dec 1980, JSN, EWV, AKW, *Nothofagus* forest; 2 females, MC, Banks Peninsula, Prices Valley, Nov 1980, RPM, Malaise trap, edge of native bush; 1 female, OL, L. Wakatipu, Bobs Cove, 23 Jan 1981, *Nothofagus* forest, mixed broadleaf, swept, JSN, EWV; 1 female, OL, Makarora W, S of N.P., 18 Jan 1981, *Nothofagus* forest, *Coprosma, Pseudowintera*, swept, JSN, EWV; 1 female, OL, L. Hawea, Kirks Bush, Jan 1987, *Nothofagus* forest, broadleaf, *P. totara*, swept, JSN, EWV; 1 female, 1 male, OL, Kinloch S.F., Dart R., Jan 1981, *Nothofagus* forest, broadleaf, grass, *P. totara*, swept, JSN, EWV; 1 female, SI, Mason Bay, 27 Feb 1968, EWV (1505); 1 female, SI, Butterfield Bay, 29 Feb 1968, EWV.

Material examined. Type series only.
ND, AK, CL, TO, TK, WN / NN, BR, MC, OL / SI.

Biology. Reared from an unidentified species of *Leucaspis*, from an unidentified eriococcid, and from a species of *Eriococcus*. J. A. deBoer recorded rearing it from "*Eriococcus hookerianus*," but I can find no such species. *Elaeocarpus hookerianus* is a host plant of *Eriococcus elaeocarpi*, a native New Zealand eriococcid (Hoy 1962), and is possibly the species alluded to.

Remarks. *Aphobetus paucisetosus* is diagnosed by the reduced number of pronotal and submarginal setae and the striate mesepimeron. The name is derived from the Latin 'paucus,' few and 'setosus,' hairy or bristly.

Genus *Moranila* Cameron

Tomocera Howard, 1881: 368. Ashmead 1904: 328. Type species *Tomocera californica* Howard, by monotypy. Preoccupied by *Tomocera* Desmarest, 1858.

Moranila Cameron, 1883: 188. Burks 1958: 75. Peck 1963: 631. Graham, 1969: 70–71. Burks 1978: 783 (and see references within for biology). Bouček 1988a: 356. Naumann 1991: 965. Type species *Moranila testaceipes* Cameron, by original monotypy.

Dilophogaster Howard, 1886: 98. Replacement name for *Tomocera* Howard.

Aphobetoideus Ashmead, 1904: 328. Type species *Aphobetoideus comperei* Ashmead, by original designation. Synonymised by Bouček (1988a: 356).

Muscidea Girault, 1915a: 323–324. Type species *Muscidea brunneiventris* Girault, by original designation. Synonymised by Bouček (1988a: 356).

Eurycraniella Girault, 1916: 227. Type species *Eurycranium baeusomorpha* Girault, by original designation. Synonymised by Bouček (1988a: 356).

Muscideoidea Girault, 1916: 227. Replacement name for *Muscidea* Girault. Synonymised by Bouček (1988a: 356).

Eunotomyia Masi, 1917: 197. Type species *Eunotomyia festiva* Masi, by monotypy. Synonymised by Burks (1958: 75).

Female. Head orange to brown, with or without discrete metallic patches or metallic lustre. Dorsal margin slightly to strongly concave. Face 1.3–1.9× as broad as long. Occipital carina weak to strong, crossed by posterior ocelli. Back of head sculptured. OD less than or equal to OOL. Vertex variously sculptured, with scattered short setae.

Antennae inserted less than 1 torular diameter above clypeal margin, moderately to strongly clavate. Scrobes smooth to entirely sculptured, carinate or not anteriorly. Club 0.7–1.5× as long as funicle. Malar groove present or absent; malar space shorter to longer than vertical axis of eye. Genal carina narrow to moderately wide, smooth or striate. Oral margin straight or curved. Genal carina and oral margin offset or not. Mandible with a broad lower tooth and 2 narrower upper teeth, sharply pointed, blunt or truncate.

Thorax from brown to orange to dark metallic green. Pronotum with setal ring comprising 8–14 setae, their bases simple, punctate, or reticulate. Mesoscutum and scapulae variously sculptured; mesoscutum with regular or paired setae, their bases simple, punctate, or reticulate. Notauli complete grooves or composed of pits. Scutellum variously shaped, flat to convex in lateral aspect, variously sculptured, with 2 pairs of setae, their bases simple, reticulate, or punctate. Frenal area variously delimited. Axillae delimited by a groove apically, by a fovea basally, smooth to sculptured, with scattered setae. Dorsellum smooth to sculptured, declivous; dorsellar fovea variously sculptured. Metanotal furrow sculptured or smooth. Mesepisternum with a triangular depression, deeper dorsally and at ventral point; mesepimeron variously sculptured or smooth, without dimples.

Forewing immaculate, or with 1 or 2 infumate patches; basal hairline infumate or not. Marginal vein 0.9–3.3× as long as stigmal vein. Stigmal area setose or bare. Postmarginal vein half as long as stigmal vein to subequal in length. Costal cell not excised to moderately excised at apex, with 0–9 setae on apex of margin; ventral row of setae complete to interrupted, and with a partial second row. Submarginal vein weakly to strongly sinuate. Basal hairline bare, or with a setal line; basal cell bare or setose; cubital hairline absent. Speculum wide or narrow; linea calva not delimited.

Hind coxae with lateral, basal, and dorsal pilosity. Hind tibiae with 1 or 2 spurs, the longest 0.1–0.5× as long as hind basitarsus.

Propodeum variously sculptured; median carina complete to nucha; costula present; nucha broader than long to square.

Gaster rectangular, circular, or oval. T1 extending 0.5–0.9× length of gaster. Basal fovea with a setal tuft at base, not extended down margin. Ovipositor exserted or not. S1 variously sculptured, not striate; base with pilosity ranging from scattered setae to compact tufts.

Male. Head broader than long, less broad than in female. Antennal insertions more or less than 1 torular diameter above clypeal margin, unbranched. Antennae with funicular segments nodose or not; F1 longer than or equal to other funicular segments; setae and sensilla long or short; club 1.5–3× as long as F1.

Forewing hyaline, or with an infumate patch. Marginal vein 1.2–2.7× as long as stigmal vein. Costal margin with 4–6 setae apically. Basal hairline with a line of setae, infumate or not; cubital hairline absent.

Biology. *Moranila* is usually a primary parasitoid, but has been recorded as a hyperparasitoid and (once) as an egg predator. *Moranila* species do not appear to be host-specific; in those species for which a number of records are available a range of families is parasitised. *M. californica* has been recorded from Coccidae, Asterolecaniidae,

Pseudococcidae, and as a hyperparasitoid through an encyrtid. *M. comperei* has been recorded from Coccidae, Pseudococcidae, Aleyrodidae (probably as a hyperparasitoid via Mymaridae), Psyllidae, and in several instances as a hyperparasitoid of Aphididae through Braconidae. Two other species have been recorded from Eriococcidae.

Distribution. One species is cosmopolitan, but is undoubtedly Australian in origin and has been introduced into North America and Europe via one of its hosts, *Saissetia oleae*. Two other commonly collected species are Australian in distribution; one of these has also been collected in New Zealand. Six species are east Australian, but are represented very poorly in the material I have examined. One species is from mainland Australia, and another from Tasmania. Two species are endemic to New Zealand.

Remarks. Seven specimens in the BPBM are close to *M. californica* but differ in propodeal sculpture in a variety of ways, with no two the same. All are from P.N.G. or the Solomons. Two specimens show moderate development (more so in one) of the anterior end of the medial carina on the propodeum, a condition almost approaching the propodeal tooth in *Aphobetus*.

Moranila aotearoae new species

Fig. 22, M16; Map 7

Female. Head shiny black, not triangular; dorsal margin slightly concave. Face 1.4× broader than long. Occipital carina weak; back of head alutaceous. Ocelli small; OD about 0.3× OOL. Vertex faintly engraved reticulate, with regular short setae.

Antennal insertions slightly more than 1 torular diameter above clypeal margin; scrobes shallow, faintly engraved reticulate, not carinate anteriorly. Antennae unicolorous orange-brown; pedicel elongate; funicular segments broader than long, but F1 square; setae short; club 1.1–1.2(1.19)× as long as funicle. Malar groove absent; malar space shorter than vertical axis of eye. Genae slightly striate; genal carina wide, not striate, with a row of setae. Oral margin slightly concave between toruli, sloping down to offset genal carina. Mandible with a broad, sharp lower tooth and 2 upper teeth.

Thorax shiny black. Pronotum broader than long, engraved reticulate, with setation reduced except for a ring of about 15 short, strong setae with bases not reticulate. Mesoscutum reduced to a narrow strip, engraved reticulate, with 2 pairs of setae between notauli, their bases not reticulate. Scapulae similarly sculptured. Notauli complete grooves. Scutellum slightly broader than long, flat in lateral aspect, engraved reticulate, with setal pairs set about the same distance apart. Frenal area delimited by a change in sculpture. Axillae delimited by a groove apically, by a deep fovea basally, faintly longitudinally striate, carinate laterally, with a posterior line of setae. Mesepimeron with a smooth, triangular depression; mesepisternum faintly transversely striate, mostly posteriorly. Dorsellum reduced to a thin, smooth strip; dorsellar fovea wide, coarsely alveolate; remainder of metanotum smooth.

Wings reduced, wedge-shaped, infumate (Fig. 22). Forewing reaching just beyond propodeum. Submarginal vein slightly sinuate. Marginal vein short. Costal cell margin convex, slightly excised at apex, with scattered ventral setae. Apical edge of wing straight, from bare to completely fringed with setae.

Legs orange-brown; coxae dark orange-brown. Hind coxae with dorsal, lateral, and basal setal crests. Hind tibial spur 0.5× as long as hind basitarsus.

Propodeum black, short, coarsely alveolate-reticulate except for a rugulose area around spiracles; nucha broader than long.

Gaster dark orange-brown. T1 engraved reticulate, extending about 0.95× length of gaster, with a compact tuft of short setae at base. Ovipositor projecting slightly beyond end of gaster. S1 with an anterior row of foveae separated from a posterior row of grooves by a wide, smooth medial area; a diffuse clump of setae medially, at base of grooves (Fig. M16).

Male. Head shiny black; clypeal area markedly convex. Antennal insertions about 2 torular diameters above clypeal margin. Antennae with funicular segments nodose, about equal in length; setae fairly sparse, about twice length of segment of origin; club about 2–2.5(2.16)× as long as F1. Forewing reduced, infumate.

Type data. Holotype (NZAC): female, "NEW ZEALAND NN/ Mt Arthur/ 1341m," "24 Mar 1971/ J. S. Dugdale/ swards 71/84," "1835."

Paratypes (11 females, 4 males; NZAC, unless otherwise noted): 1 female, NN, L. Sylvester, Iron Hill, 1600 m, 18 Nov 1972, JSD, litter 72/193; 2 males, NN, Mt Domett, 30 Nov 1971, GK, mat plants, 71/164; 1 female, NN, Mt Domett, 1250 m, 30 Nov 1971, GK, litter 71/174; 1 female, MB, Richmond Range, Mt Johnson, 1585 m, 13 Mar 1969, JSD, litter 69/89; 1 female, MB, Black Birch Range, Mt Altimarlock, 1670 m, 16 Feb 1970, GK, plants 70/121; 2 females, BR, Mt Robert, 15 Mar 1968, WWV, 1521; 1 female, BR, Paparoa Range, Mt Dewar, 1697 m, 2 Dec 1969, JIT, mat, plants, 69/238; 1 male, BR, Paparoa Range, Mt Dewar, 1310 m, Lochnagar Ridge, 10 Dec 1969, JSD, swards, 69/247; 2 females, CO, Rocklands Stn, 800 m,

Feb–Mar 1979, BIPB, pit trap in tussock (1 ANIC); 1 female, CO, Grandview Pk, 1433 m, 12 Jan 1971, JSD, swards 71/12; 1 male, CO, Dunstan Range, 1585 m, 13 Jan 1971, JSD, swards 71/3.

Material examined. Type series only.
— / NN, MB, BR, CO.

Biology. Hosts are unknown.

Remarks. *Moranila aotearoae* is diagnosed by its reduced, wedge-shaped, infumate forewing.

Moranila californica (Howard)

Fig. M17; Map 8

californica Howard, 1881: 368 (*Tomocera*); —1886: 98 (*Dilophogaster*). Smith & Compere 1928: 317–321, fig. 55-57 (*Tomocera*). Burks 1958: 75 (*Moranila*). Peck 1963: 631. Valentine 1967: 1128. Graham 1969: 70–71. Burks 1978: 783. Bouček 1988a: 356–357 (*Dilophogaster, Tomocera, Moranila*). Morales 1989: 237–239 (*Moranila*). Valentine & Walker 1991: 28.

testaceipes Cameron, 1883: 188–189 (*Moranila*). Burks 1958: 75; —1978: 783. Bouček 1988a: 357. Synonymised by Howard (1896: 165).

ceroplastis Perkins, 1906: 76 (*Tomocera*). Bouček 1988a: 357. Synonymised by Burks (1978: 783).

glabriventris Girault, 1915b: 207–208 (*Tomocera*); — 1927: 334. Dahms 1984: 651. Bouček 1988a: 357. Synonymised by Burks (1978: 783).

flaviceps Girault, 1915b: 208 (*Tomocera*). Dahms 1984: 603. Bouček 1988a: 357. Synonymised by Burks (1978: 783).

festiva Masi, 1917: 195–197 (*Eunotomyia*). Synonymised by Bouček (1988a: 357).

Female. Head not strongly triangular, orange-brown with genal carina metallic green and with 2 metallic green spots directly behind eyes; dorsal margin deeply concave. Face 1.4–1.7(1.56)× broader than long. Occipital carina complete; back of head alutaceous. OD about 0.75× OOL. Vertex alutaceous, with scattered short setae.

Antennal insertions less than half a torular diameter above clypeal margin; scrobes smooth, very weakly carinate anteriorly. Antennae with scape orange-brown, pedicel and flagellum brown; F1 to F4 as long as broad, F5 broader than long; setae short; club 0.8–1.0(0.92)× as long as funicle. Genae smooth; genal carina narrow, not striate, but with a row of setae. Malar groove absent; malar space as long as vertical axis of eye. Oral margin between toruli straight, sloping down to offset genal carina. Mandible with a broad, pointed lower tooth and 2 upper teeth, 1 pointed and 1 blunt.

Thorax dark metallic green, engraved reticulate. Pronotum sculptured, with regular short setation and a ring of 8 long, strong setae; setal bases reticulate. Mesoscutum engraved reticulate, with 2–4 pairs of setae between notauli; setal bases reticulate, the reticulation sometimes inconspicuous in smaller specimens. Notauli complete grooves. Scapulae engraved reticulate, wide, with 2 pairs of setae. Scutellum as long as broad, convex in lateral aspect, alutaceous; anterior pair of setae closer together than posterior pair. Frenal area delimited by a very faint line; sculpture becoming less dense towards apex. Axillae delimited by a groove apically, by a fovea basally. Axillae smooth and shiny, unsculptured, each with only 1 conspicuous seta, carinate laterally. Mesepisternum with a triangular depression, deeper dorsally and at ventral point; mesepimeron smooth. Dorsellum smooth, with dorsellar fovea alveolate; remainder of metanotum smooth; furrow non-striate.

Forewing with a large infumate patch extending from basal hairline to well beyond stigmal vein, and with infumation along apical cubital hairline. Marginal vein 1.2–1.5(1.29)× as long as stigmal vein. Postmarginal vein half as long as stigmal vein. Stigmal area sparsely setose. Costal cell slightly excised at apex, with 3 or 4 setae on apex of margin; ventral row of setae broadly interrupted, with no partial second row. Submarginal vein sinuate. Basal hairline not infumate, with a single seta or none; basal cell bare.

Legs and coxae orange, but middle tibiae brown, and hind leg brown dorsally. Middle tarsal segments whitish, fore and hind yellow. Hind coxae with conspicuous dorsal, lateral, basal, and ventral crests. Hind tibiae with 2 spurs, the longer 0.3× as long as basitarsus.

Propodeum dark brown-black; medial areas posterior to costula, anterior to nucha, and around spiracles smooth and shiny. Nucha as long as broad, globose, alveolate-reticulate basally and irregularly rugulose apically.

Gaster dark red-brown, rectangular. T1 extending about 0.9x length of gaster. Basal fovea short, shallow, with a compact setal tuft at base. Ovipositor short, scarcely projecting beyond end of gaster. T1 with or without 2 oval matt areas. Upper area of S1 broadly concave, with vague grooves laterally; medial area wide, flat, pitted; posteriorly a row of grooves as long as broad medially, longer laterally. Sparse setae at base of medial groove (Fig. M17).

Male. Head very dark red-brown to black, with metallic blue lustre.

Antennal insertions almost 2 torular diameters above clypeal margin. Antennae unicolorous mid-brown; funicular segments strongly nodose; F1 slightly longer than other funicular segments; setae arranged in clumps, on F1 to F3 at least twice as long as segment of origin, on F4 about equal, and on club much shorter; sensilla moderately long; club 1.7× as long as F1.

Thorax dark red-brown to black. Forewing hyaline. Marginal vein 1–1.1× as long as stigmal vein. Costal cell margined with setae along distal 50–60%; ventral setal row continuous with a partial second row. Basal hairline not pigmented, comprising 4 or 5 setae; basal cell bare; cubital hairline absent.

Gaster dark red-brown.

Type data. *californica*: type material from Los Angeles, California, not seen.

testaceipes: type material from Oahu, Hawai'i, not seen.

ceroplastis: type material from Cairns, Qld, not seen.

glabriventris: holotype female (SAMA). The card-mounted holotype body and additional material listed in the description (two females from Gordonvale and one from Chindera) are lost. The only remnant of the holotype in QMBA is a slide with two coverslip fragments covering the head, with one complete and one incomplete antenna, one leg, two forewings, and one hind wing, labelled "TYPE, Hy/3198, A. A. Girault," "Queensland Museum/ [f] *Tomocera glabriventris* Gir." Further material identified by Girault as *T. glabriventris* is deposited in QMBA (two females from Montville, Qld) and SAMA (one female from Cornwallis Island, Torres Straits); none of this material has type status. Publication data: "*Habitat:* Gordonvale (Cairns), Queensland. Jungle, November 1 1913 (A.P.D.). *Type:* No. *Hy 3198,* Queensland Museum, Brisbane, the female on a tag; head and a hind leg on a slide."

flaviceps: type material not seen. Publication data: "Described from three females reared from a coccid. October 10. 1913 (G. F. Hill). Labelled 'No.24.' *Habitat*: Port Darwin. Northern Territory. Types: No. *Hy 3199,* Queensland Museum. Brisbane. Three females on a tag."

festiva: lectotype from Mahé, Seychelles, not seen (BMNH).

Material examined. Ten non-type females (NZAC). **AK**. Lynfield, 17 May 1975, G.K. (1). Massey, 26 Mar 1975, EWV, *Saissetia coffeae* eggs (1). Oakleigh [?Oakley Creek, AK], mangrove, on *Ceroplastes sinensis*, Feb 1971, RAC (1). **NN**. Nelson, 16–19 Mar 1965, BBG, ex *Saissetia oleae* on grapefruit leaf (1006) (3). Nelson, 20 Feb 1963, BBG, ex *Saissetia oleae* immature on *Prostanthera* (660) (1). Nelson, 6–15 Feb 1960, EWV, ex *Saissetia oleae* (3). AK / NN.

Also examples from Australia (72 females, 20 males, mostly ANIC), Cook Islands (1 female, NZAC), Samoa (1 female, BMNH), Tonga (1 female, BMNH), Papua New Guinea (1 female, BMNH), Hawaii (1 female, BMNH), Sandwich Is (1 female, BMNH), Mauritius (1 female, BMNH), Admiralty Is (2 females, BMNH), Seychelles (1 female, BMNH), Italy (1 female, NZAC), Israel (1 female, BMNH), and U.S.A. (1 female, BMNH).

Biology. Berry (1994) records as hosts of *M. californica*: *Saissetia oleae* on mandarin, lemon (*Citrus limon*), *Osteospermum moniliferum*, and oleander (*Nerium oleander*); *Ceroplastes sinensis* on grapefruit; *Ceroplastes* sp.; immature *Saissetia oleae* on *Prostanthera*; *Saissetia coffeae* eggs; *Parasaissetia* (=*Saissetia*) *nigra* on cassava; and *Coccus* (=*Lecanium*) on frangipani.

Graham (1969) records *M. californica* as a parasitoid of scale insects, particularly Coccidae, especially *Saissetia* and *Ceroplastes* spp., and rarely as a hyperparasitoid through encyrtids. Peck (1963) records it from an unidentified *Asterolecanium* species, *Chaetococcus* (=*Antonina*) *bambusae*, *Coccus hesperidum*, *Saissetia hemisphaerica* (=*S. coffeae*), and as a hyperparasitoid through *Microterys flavus*. Burks (1978) describes it as an egg predator and, rarely, a hyperparasitoid. Smith & Compere (1928) record *Asterolecanium pustulans* and *Ceroplastes rubens* as hosts of *M. californica*; and Mercet (in Compere & Smith 1928) lists *Ceroplastes rusci* and *C. sinensis* as hosts in Spain. Bouček (1988a) lists *Ceroplastes ceriferus* as a host.

Distribution. Cosmopolitan. Smith & Compere (1928) consider that *M. californica* is native to Australia but arrived in California with one of its hosts, *S. oleae*, and became more widespread there than in its native country. It is rarely collected in Australia.

Remarks. *Moranila californica* is diagnosed by the two metallic green spots behind the occipital carina and the distinctive sculpture of the propodeum.

Moranila comperei (Ashmead)

Fig. 12, 13, 23, M18, M19; Map 9

comperei Ashmead, 1904: 328 (*Aphobetoideus*). Smith & Compere 1928: 312–317, fig. 51–54. Gahan & Peck 1946: 314. Bouček 1988a: 357, fig. 662, 663 (*Moranila*). Valentine & Walker 1991: 28.
io Girault, 1929: 319–320 (*Tomocera*). Dahms 1984: 728. Bouček 1988a: 357 (*Moranila*). New synonymy.
saissetiae Girault, 1925b: 2–3 (*Tomocera*). Dahms 1986: 498. Bouček 1988a: 357 (*Moranila*). New synonymy.

transversifasciata Girault, 1925a: 91 (*Tomocera*). Dahms 1986: 592. Bouček 1988a: 357 (*Moranila*). New synonymy.

Female. Head orange, metallic green and/or purple around ocelli, not strongly triangular, more square; dorsal margin slightly concave. Face 1.3–1.5(1.39)× as broad as long. Occipital carina weak; back of head alutaceous. OD about 0.75× OOL. Vertex alutaceous, with scattered short setae.

Antennal insertions less than half a torular diameter above clypeal margin; scrobes smooth, not carinate anteriorly. Antennae (Fig. 12) with scape orange, pedicel and flagellum brown; F1 from slightly broader than long to square; F2 from longer than broad to square; F3 to F5 more or less square; club 0.7–1(0.84)× as long as funicle. Genae smooth; genal carina moderately wide, coarsely striate, metallic green. Malar groove complete; malar space subequal to vertical axis of eye. Oral margin very slightly concave between toruli, sloping very gently to offset genal carina. Mandible with a broad lower tooth and 2 narrow upper teeth.

Thorax dark metallic green. Pronotum imbricate, with regular short setation and a ring of 10–14 long, strong setae with bases not reticulate. Mesoscutum imbricate, with few to numerous scattered short setae and a pair of setae (posteriorly) between notauli, their bases not reticulate. Notauli complete, composed of defined grooves. Scapulae sculptured similarly to mesonotum. Scutellum subsquare, slightly convex in lateral aspect, engraved reticulate to almost smooth, with a very faint engraved reticulate pattern discernible; anterior pair of setae closer together than posterior pair; setal bases not reticulate. Frenal area faintly delimited by a change in sculpture to almost smooth. Axillae delimited by a groove apically, by a fovea basally, smooth, with scattered setae. Mesepisternum with a triangular depression, deeper dorsally and at ventral point; mesepimeron mainly smooth, with some slight transverse striation. Dorsellum smooth, declivous; dorsellar fovea alveolate; remainder of metanotum smooth; furrow non-striate.

Forewings (Fig. 23) with a large, central infumate patch. Marginal vein 2.1–3.3(2.69)× as long as stigmal vein. Stigmal area sparsely setose or bare. Postmarginal vein 0.9× as long as stigmal vein. Costal cell slightly excised at apex, with 2 setae on apex of margin; ventral row of setae narrowly interrupted, with a partial second row. Submarginal vein slightly sinuate. Basal hairline not infumate, bare; basal cell bare.

Legs orange, but middle and hind tibiae brown. Hind tibiae with 2 spurs, the longer 0.2× as long as hind basitarsus. Hind coxae with lateral, basal, and sparse dorsal setal crests.

Propodeum dark metallic green, regularly reticulate anterior to costula and irregularly reticulate posterior to costula, with a smooth triangular plate at base of median carina, smooth around spiracles, with a long setal tuft; nucha broader than long.

Gaster rectangular, from orange grading to brown apically to dark brown excepting mid-brown base. T1 extending 0.5–0.6× length of gaster. Basal fovea short, shallow, with a compact setal tuft at base. Ovipositor projecting beyond end of gaster. S1 anteriorly with 2 rows of foveae separated by narrow ridges, posteriorly grooved, the grooves longer than broad, with sparse scattered setae in bases of medial 4 grooves (Fig. M18, M19).

Male. Head orange-brown to brown with metallic blue and/or purple lustre on vertex, grading to orange around mouth, slightly less broad, about 1.2× as broad as long.

Antennal insertions higher, at least 1 torular diameter above clypeal margin. Antennae (Fig. 13) with scape and pedicel orange, flagellum orange to brown; F1 to F4 similar in size, strongly nodose; setae about as long as segment of origin; sensilla conspicuous, as long as segment of origin; club 1.7–2.8(2.05)× as long as F1.

Forewing with a faint central infumate patch. Marginal vein 2.0–2.7(2.28)× as long as stigmal vein. Costal margin with about 5 setae apically. Basal hairline not infumate, with 0–2 setae; basal cell sparsely setose.

Gaster ranging from medium brown in anterior half and dark brown in posterior half to yellow-brown in anterior half and dark brown in posterior half, with 2 dark brown patches adjacent to basal fovea.

Type data. *comperei*: Type specimens were never designated by Ashmead, the species description occurs in the key only. Bouček (1988a) cites Swan River, W.A. as a collection locality. It is unclear whether he regards this as the original collecting locality, and if so, how he determined it.

io: holotype female (SAMA) on a card labelled "Type," "Tomocera/ io/ Girault. Type [f]," "Tomocera/ io Girault/ South Australia/ also Slide/ TYPE," "S. A. Museum/ Specimen" and a slide labelled "TYPE," "Ent.Div./ Dep.Ag & Stk., Qld./ Tomocera/ io Girault Type [f]/ No. S. Aus. Mus." One complete coverslip covering 1 female forewing and 2 female antennae (fragmented), and half a coverslip with head. Publication details: "A female, from galls on leaves of *Eucalyptus obliqua*, Blakiston, South Australia (T. D. Smeaton). Hatched May, 1888."

saissetiae: holotype female (QMBA) on a slide labelled "HOLOTYPE/ T.9890/ E.C.D. 1985," "Tomocera/ flaviceps Gir./ [f] type (inner)," "[f]/ Tomocera/ saissetiae Gir./ Type (outer)." An almost complete coverslip with 1

leg and female forewing (*flaviceps*); a part coverslip with female gaster, parts of thorax, 1 female antennal club, and 1 wing, and a part coverslip with 1 leg, 1 head, and 1 antenna minus club (*saissetiae*). Publication data: "A female, Wahroonga, N.S.Wales, on *Saissetia oleae*, May 23, W. B. Gurney."

transversifasciata: a holotype was not designated, so the remaining type material has the status of syntypes. Lectotype female (QMBA) here designated, on a slide labelled "SYNTYPES/ T.10017/ E.C.D. 1985," "Epitetracnemus [f]/ auricornis Gir./ Type," "Tomocera/ transversifasci-/ ata Gir./ [f] [m] types." A complete coverslip with 1 syntype female with head and some legs separated (designated lectotype), and head and 1 pair of wings from another type specimen (designated paralectotype; head lacking part of 1 antenna); 1 complete but cracked coverslip containing *E. auricornis* Girault. Publication data: "Several pairs, damp forest, Wynnum, Queensland, November 4 1921."

Material examined. Type specimens as listed above, plus 4 non-type examples (3 females, 1 male, NZAC), AK, New Lynn, Lynmall, 4 Apr 1994, N.A. Martin, ex *Nipaecoccus aurilanatus* on *Araucaria heterophylla*.

AK / —.

Also examples from Australia (28 females, 25 males, mostly ANIC).

Biology. *M. comperei* has been reared from *Cavariella aegopodii*/*Aphidius salicis* on carrot; *Diaeretiella rapae* in *Brevicoryne brassicae*; *Myzus persicae* on kale (*Brassica oleracea* var. *acephala*); *Aphidius colemani* and *Ephedrus persicae* in *Myzus persicae* on peach (*Prunus persica*); *Lipaphis erisimi* / *Diaeretiella rapae* on canola; *Eriosoma lanigerum* on apple (*Malus sylvestris*); aphid mummies; Mymaridae / *Trialeurodes vaporariorum* ; *Ctenarytaina thysanura* on *Boronia megastigma*; *Saissetiae oleae* on lemon; and *Nipaecoccus aurilanatus* mummies on *Araucaria heterophylla*.

Smith & Compere (1928) assume that *M. comperei* is usually a primary parasitoid of coccoids, but Bouček (1988a) records it as reared from a mummified aphid on peach (A.C.T) and from *M. persicae*. Smith & Compere (1928) reared *M. comperei* from *S. oleae*; but they also recorded a pupa of *M. comperei* inhabiting the body of a scale in company with a pupa of *Metaphycus lounsburyi* (Encyrtidae), and concluded that this indicates facultative hyperparasitism.

Distribution. Recorded from Western Australia, South Australia, Australian Capital Territory, Victoria, and Tasmania, as well as New Zealand.

Remarks. *Moranila comperei* is diagnosed by the distinctive sculpture of the propodeum, particularly the smooth triangular plate at the base of the median carina. Specimens can be divided into two groups on the basis of whether the scutellum is smooth or sculptured. However, since the other diagnostic characters vary, and reared series have specimens falling into both groups, I cannot justify separating these specimens into two morphospecies. *Bouček* identified as *M. comperei* five specimens with the scutellum sculptured and one with the scutellum smooth, but he also identified some New Zealand material of an undoubtedly different species as *comperei*.

Moranila strigaster new species

Fig. 2, 14, 24, M20; Map 10

Female (Fig. 2). Head from very dark red-brown without metallic lustre to black with metallic blue and/or purple lustre, not triangular; dorsal margin moderately concave. Face 1.5–1.8(1.6)× as broad as long. Occipital carina complete but weak; back of head alutaceous. Ocelli small; OD about 0.4× OOL. Vertex faintly engraved reticulate, with scattered short setae.

Antennal insertions about 1.5 torular diameters above clypeal margin; scrobes shallow and smooth, not carinate anteriorly. Antennae unicolorous orange to medium brown; pedicel elongate; F1 and F2 slightly broader than long to square; other funicular segments longer than broad or square; club 0.8–1.1(0.93)× as long as funicle (Fig. 14). Genae smooth; genal carina wide, not striate, with a row of setae. Malar groove complete but inconspicuous, its remnant deep; malar space shorter than vertical axis of eye. Oral margin straight between toruli, sloping down to offset genal carina. Mandible with a broad, sharp lower tooth and 2 upper teeth.

Thorax from black with metallic lustre to very dark red-brown without metallic lustre. Pronotum broader than long, faintly engraved reticulate, sparsely setose, with a ring of about 8 short, pale setae, their bases not reticulate. Mesoscutum faintly engraved reticulate, with 2 pairs of short setae between notauli, their bases not reticulate. Notauli complete grooves. Scapulae faintly engraved reticulate. Scutellum as long as broad, flat in lateral aspect engraved reticulate; anterior pair of setae slightly closer together than posterior pair. Frenal area only very faintly delimited by a change in sculpture. Axillae delimited by a groove apically, by a deep fovea basally, faintly longitudinally striate, carinate laterally. Mesopleuron with a smooth triangular depression; mesepisternum faintly transversely striate, mostly posteriorly. Dorsellum smooth; dorsellar fovea coarsely alveolate; remainder of metanotum smooth.

Forewing (Fig. 24) with a small, faint to larger, dark infumate patch. Marginal vein 1.7–2.7(2.22)× as long as stigmal vein. Postmarginal vein 0.8× as long as stigmal vein. Stigmal area bare. Costal cell slightly excised at apex, with 2 setae dorsally at apex of margin; ventral row of setae continuous, with a partial second row. Submarginal vein only slightly sinuate. Basal hairline not infumate, bare; basal cell bare; cubital hairline absent. Setation on disc sparse.

Legs from yellow with brown tibiae to entirely brown. Hind coxae with dorsal, lateral, and basal setal crests. Hind tibial spur 0.2× as long as hind basitarsus.

Propodeum black with a faint blue sheen to very dark red-brown without metallic lustre, entirely coarsely alveolate-reticulate except for a rugose strip on apex; area around spiracles smooth and shiny; nucha short.

Gaster dark red-brown, paler apically. T1 extending about 0.9× length of gaster, coarsely longitudinally striate over most of surface, with a compact setal tuft at base. Ovipositor projecting slightly beyond end of gaster. S1 with 2 rows of foveae separated by a medial smooth, narrow ridge; medial posterior foveae with a large tuft of foliaceous setae basally (Fig. M20).

Male. Head black, with slight blue metallic lustre.

Antennal insertions at lower ocular level, about 2 torular diameters above clypeal margin. Antennae with scape, pedicel, and flagellum orange-brown; funicular segments very long and nodose, subequal in length; setae very long, at least 2× segment of origin; club about 1.5–1.8(1.64)× as long as F1.

Frenal area delimited by a change in sculpture. Forewing with very faint infumation. Marginal vein 2.0–2.2(2.1)× as long as stigmal vein. Costal cell with about 5 setae on apical margin. Basal hairline infumate, with 1 seta; cubital hairline absent.

Striations on T1 less conspicuous.

Type data. Holotype (NZAC): female, "NEW ZEALAND NN/ Mt Domett/ N. W. Nelson 1250m," "30 Nov 1971/ G. Kuschel/ litter 71/167."

Paratypes (10 females, 2 males; NZAC unless otherwise noted): 1 female, NN, Mt Fell, 13 Mar 1969, EWV 1689; 2 females, 1 male, BR, Mt Robert, 15 Mar 1968, EWV 1521; 1 female, 1 male, NC, Arthurs Pass, 9 Feb 1978, tussock, em[erged] 20 Feb 1978, AKW; 2 females (1 ANIC), MK, L. Tekapo, Dec 1980, PQ, Malaise trap in tussock near pine plantation; 1 female, OL, Coronet Peak, 1200 m, Jan 1981, tussock, grasses, *Hebe*, alpine shrubs, swept, JSN, EWV; 1 female, CO, Rocklands Stn, 800 m, Apr 1979, BIPB, pit trap in tussock; 1 female, CO, Old Man Range, 1372 m, 20 Nov 1974, JCW, mixed moss and tussock 74/96; 1 female, SI, Mason Bay, 27 Feb 1968, EWV 1505.

Material examined. Type series only.
— / NN, BR, NC, MK, OL, CO / SI.

Biology. Hosts are unknown.

Remarks. *Moranila strigaster* is diagnosed by the coarsely longitudinally striate surface of T1. Specimens fall into two groups, one comprising females with a metallic lustre and yellow antennae and legs, no transverse funicular segments, and more definite propodeal sculpture, and the other females without a metallic lustre, with darker antennae and legs, with F1 and F2 broader than long, and with somewhat reduced propodeal sculpture. Collection of further material may allow *M. strigaster* to be divided into two species.

The name *strigaster* refers to the striate sculpture of the first gastral tergite.

Genus *Ophelosia* Riley

Ophelosia Riley, 1890: 249. Ashmead 1904: 328. Valentine 1967: 1129. Bouček 1988a: 353–354. Charles 1989: 226–227. Naumann 1991: 965. Type species *Ophelosia crawfordi* Riley, by original monotypy.

Asaphomorphella Girault, 1913: 104–105. Type species *Asaphomorphella rousseaui* Girault, by original designation. Synonymised by Bouček (1988a).

Female. Head orange-brown, with or without metallic lustre; dorsal margin weakly to moderately concave. Face 1.3–1.9× broader than long. Occipital carina weak to strong. Ocelli removed from margin by 0.1–1.0× OD; OD less than OOL to subequal. Vertex variously sculptured, with scattered short to long setae.

Antennal insertions less than 1 torular diameter above clypeal margin; scrobes not carinate to moderately carinate anteriorly, smooth to entirely sculptured. Antennae with club 0.6–1.3× as long as funicle. Malar groove present or absent; malar space 0.5–1.3× vertical axis of eye. Genae smooth to sculptured; genal carina narrow to wide, striate or not, offset or not offset from clypeal margin. Oral margin variously shaped; clypeus produced or not. Mandible with a broad lower tooth and 2 narrow upper teeth.

Thorax from orange to dark orange-brown, with or without metallic green reflections. Pronotum 2–4× as broad as long; setal ring with 8–14 setae, their bases simple. Mesoscutum variously sculptured, with regular and paired setae or paired setae only, their bases simple. Notauli

complete grooves. Scapulae variously sculptured. Scutellum about as long as wide, flat to slightly convex in lateral aspect, variously sculptured, with 2 pairs of setae. Frenal area delimited or not, if so then only by a faint line or change in sculpture, never by a groove. Axillae variously sculptured. Mesepisternum with a shallow triangular depression; mesepimeron smooth to sculptured, without dimples. Dorsellum sculptured or not, declivous; fovea rugose to alveolate; metanotal furrow smooth to coarsely striate.

Forewing complete or variously reduced. Complete wing with a faint to dark infumate patch posterior to stigmal vein and distal marginal vein. Marginal vein 1.7–4.6× as long as stigmal vein. Stigmal area bare to sparsely setose. Postmarginal vein slightly shorter than stigmal vein to slightly longer. Costal cell very slightly excised at apex, with 1–15 setae on distal margin; ventral line of setae complete or interrupted, with or without a partial second line. Basal hairline with a line, strip, or long tuft of setae, faintly or strongly infumate; basal cell bare or with scattered setae; cubital setal line present or absent. Speculum narrow to wide; linea calva not delimited. Marginal fringe moderately long.

Hind tibial spur (0.6–)0.8–1.2× as long as hind basitarsus. Hind coxae variously setose.

Propodeum with median carina present anteriorly, absent posteriorly; costula present laterally to almost absent; surface variously rugose / reticulate / alveolate, smooth to sculptured around spiracles; nucha square or longer than broad, smooth or sculptured at apex, with apical margin weakly to deeply emarginate medially.

Gaster variously setose at base, the setae not extended down margin of fovea. T1 extending 0.5–0.9× length of gaster. S1 with collar variously sculptured anteriorly, grooved posteriorly; surface not striate; setae absent.

Male. Antennal insertions from slightly less to slightly more than 1 torular diameter above clypeal margin. Funicular segments variable in relative length; setae short to long; club 1.0–6.4× as long as F1.

Forewing hyaline or weakly to strongly infumate under distal marginal and stigmal veins. Basal hairline weakly to strongly infumate, with a line, strip, or tuft of setae; cubital hairline infumate or not. Marginal vein 1.5–5.2× as long as stigmal vein. Postmarginal vein subequal in length to stigmal vein.

Biology. *Ophelosia* includes primary parasitoids and egg predators of margarodids and pseudococcids, and occasional hyperparasitoids. Some species—e.g., *O. crawfordi* and *O. hypatia*—are host-specific and niche-specific to the extent of being exclusively egg predators of *Icerya*. Others, most notably *O. bifasciata*, are more general, behaving as egg predators and parasitoids and also on occasion as hyperparasitoids via encyrtids on pseudococcids or aphids. *O. charlesi* is almost exclusively a predator of pseudococcid ovisacs, but there are some records from New Zealand of it behaving as a parasitoid of *Pseudococcus* species.

Distribution. *Ophelosia* has been recorded from North America, India, Papua New Guinea, Java, Australia, and New Zealand. It undoubtedly occurs throughout Asia but has not been collected. *Ophelosia crawfordi* occurs in North America, presumably having been introduced along with its host, *Icerya purchasi*, as well as in Java, eastern Australia, and New Zealand. Two species appear to be endemic to P.N.G. but are represented by only one specimen each. Of the more widespread species, *O. bifasciata* is distributed throughout Australia, New Zealand, and P.N.G.; and *O. keatsi* occurs in Australia and New Zealand. Two brachypterous and one narrow-winged species are endemic to New Zealand. Two species are found throughout mainland Australia and Tasmania, two in eastern Australia, one in eastern Australia and Tasmania, and one in eastern Australia and New Zealand. One species is restricted to Western Australia and one to Tasmania.

Ophelosia australis new species

Fig. 15, 25, M22; Map 11

Female. Head orange-brown; dorsal margin weakly concave. Face 1.4–1.6(1.52)× broader than long. Occipital carina weak. Ocelli removed from margin by slightly less than 1 OD; OD about 0.75× OOL. Vertex alutaceous, with scattered long setae.

Antennal insertions slightly less than one torular diameter above clypeal margin; scrobes not sculptured, not carinate anteriorly. Antennae with scape orange, pedicel and flagellum medium brown; funicular segments broader than long; club 0.7–1.0(0.87)× as long as funicle. Lower face smooth. Malar groove complete, inconspicuous; malar space 0.5× long axis of eye. Genal carina narrow, not striate. Clypeal margin slightly produced; oral margin concave between toruli, sloping to offset genal carina. Mandible with a sharp lower tooth and 2 blunt upper teeth.

Thorax orange-brown. Pronotum alutaceous, with short regular setae and a ring of about 10 setae, smooth posterior to ring. Mesoscutum broader than long, imbricate, with sparse regular setae and a pair of long setae at scutellar boundary. Scapulae imbricate. Scutellum broader than long, flat in lateral aspect, engraved reticulate. Frenal area not delimited, except by a change in sculpture to smooth in posterior quarter. Axillae smooth. Dorsellum reduced,

smooth; metanotal furrow reduced, alveolate; remainder of metanotum smooth. Mesepisternum with a triangular depression; mesepimeron smooth.

Forewing (Fig. 25) reduced, reaching slightly past propodeum, with submarginal and marginal veins present, stigmal and postmarginal veins absent. Disc setose, very reduced, with about 13 setae. Wing weakly infumate, more strongly at cubital hairline, basal hairline, and distally. Costal cell reduced to a thin strip, with no setae on apical margin but some ventral setae. Setae on submarginal and marginal veins very long; submarginal vein with 2 setae. Basal hairline infumate; basal cell bare, not margined by cubital hairline. Wing fringed distally.

Legs orange. Hind coxae with sparse dorsal, basal, and lateral setal crests. Hind tibial spur 0.8× as long as hind basitarsus.

Propodeum orange-brown; median carina present anteriorly; costula present laterally. Sculpture rugose-reticulate, smooth around spiracles and on apex of nucha. Nucha broader than long, very shallowly emarginate apically. Tuft of setae at spiracles long, conspicuous.

Gaster orange-brown. Basal fovea with scattered setae at base. T1 extending 0.6× length of abdomen. Ovipositor exserted. S1 with moderately spaced long grooves, interrupted medially by a smooth horizontal ridge (Fig. M22).

Male. Head dark red-brown with faint purple metallic lustre. OD about 0.5× OOL. Antennal insertions 1 torular diameter above clypeal margin, unicolorous mid-brown. Antennae (Fig. 15) with F1 the longest flagellar segment; F2 to F4 subequal, slightly longer than broad; setae shorter than segment of origin; club 1.6–2.0(1.76)× as long as F1.

Thorax orange-brown with a faint purple-green metallic lustre. Forewing reduced, reaching slightly past propodeum, fringed posteriorly and distally. Submarginal and marginal veins present; stigmal vein rudimentary; postmarginal vein absent. Disc reduced, with at least 50 setae. Basal hairline not infumate, with 1 or 2 setae. Costal cell reduced, scarcely excised at apex, with 6 setae on apical margin. Speculum present; linea calva absent. Legs orange brown, with sparse lateral, dorsal, and basal crests of setae.

Propodeum and gaster orange-brown.

Type data. Holotype (NZAC): female, MB, "Upcot saddle/ 2750' 28.ix.65/ J. I. Townsend," "Moss in Tussock/ and pasture."

Paratypes (10 females, 3 males; NZAC, unless otherwise noted): 3 males, BR, S Victoria Range nr Rahu Sdle, 1310 m, 27 Jan 1972, JCW, litter and moss; 1 female (LUNZ), NC, Arthurs Pass, 915 m, 14–23 Apr 1984, JWE, yellow pan in subalpine scrub; 1 female, MC, Hunters Hills, Rd to Meyer's Pass, 430 m, 20 Jan 1966, GWR, in moss; 2 females, CO, Lindis Pass, 971 m, 11 Jan 1971, JSD, litter 71/9; 4 females (1 ANIC), CO, Rocklands Stn, 800 m and 400 m, Apr 1979 and 14–28 Dec 1979, B.I.P. Barratt, pit trap in tussock; 1 female, DN, Wairoa, 5–12 Dec 1979, BIPB, pit trap in tussock; 1 female, SL, Hokonui Hills, 365 m, S[ad]dle W [of] Dollamore Park, 2 May 1968, JCW, litter.

Material examined. Type series only.
— / MB, BR, NC, MC, CO, DN, SL.

Biology. Hosts unknown.

Remarks. *Ophelosia australis* is diagnosed by its reduced forewing, particularly the reduced disc with less than 20 setae, and the lack of a vestigial stigmal vein.

Ophelosia bifasciata Girault

Fig. 16, M23–26; Map 12

bifasciata Girault, 1916: 228 (*Ophelosia*). Dahms 1983: 136–137. Bouček 1988a: 354.
rousseaui Girault, 1913: 104–105 (*Asaphomorphella*). Dahms 1986: 480. Bouček 1988a: 354 (*Ophelosia*). New synonymy.
viridinotata Girault, 1916: 228 (*Ophelosia*). Dahms 1986: 639. Bouček 1988a: 354. New synonymy.

Female. Head orange-brown, grading to dark brown along occipital carina; dorsal margin deeply concave. Face 1.3–1.7(1.45)× broader than long. Occipital carina strong; ocelli less than 0.1 OD from carina; OD greater than OOL. Back of head alutaceous. Vertex finely transversely striate, with scattered long setae. Eyes minutely hairy.

Antennal insertions less than half a torular diameter above clypeal margin; scrobes smooth (Fig. M23), weakly to rather strongly carinate anteriorly. Antennae (Fig. 16) with scape orange-brown, pedicel and flagellum dark brown; F1 broader than long, F2 to F4 square, F5 slightly broader than long; setae short; club 0.8–1.0(0.89)× as long as funicle. Malar groove complete; malar space 0.5× long axis of eye. Genae smooth and shiny; genal carina narrow, not striate, with a row of setae. Clypeus slightly produced. Oral margin between toruli straight, sloping down to offset genal carina (Fig. M23, M24). Mandibles with a pointed lower tooth and 2 rounded upper teeth.

Thorax ranging from entirely orange-brown with very faint metallic green/blue/purple reflections through orange-brown with dark brown markings and a strong metallic lustre (often on axillae and frenum, or medially dark) to entirely dark brown. Pronotum imbricate anterior to setal ring, alutaceous posterior to it, with a ring of 10–12 setae. Mesoscutum imbricate, covered with regular pilosity, and with a pair of long setae at posterior end. Scapulae alutaceous, with several pairs of setae and regular pilosity. Scutellum slightly convex in lateral aspect, more or less square, alutaceous; anterior pair of setae closer together than posterior pair. Frenal area delimited only by a change of sculpture to mainly smooth with faint longitudinal striations. Axillae smooth, with very prominent metallic reflections and with several pairs of setae. Dorsellum smooth; dorsellar fovea alveolate; metanotum smooth; metanotal furrow coarsely striate. Mesepisternum with a very shallow depression, slightly striate; mesepimeron smooth.

Forewing with a large, diffuse infumate patch posterior to marginal and stigmal veins. Marginal vein 2.3–3.5(2.8)× as long as stigmal vein. Postmarginal vein subequal in length to stigmal vein. Stigmal area sparsely setose. Submarginal vein with about 8 setae. Costal cell with 1–3 setae on apex of margin. Ventral row of setae broadly interrupted medially to narrowly interrupted medially to continuous, with a partial second row. Basal hairline infumate, with a triangular tuft of more than 40 dark setae, the upper setae as long as proximal submarginal setae, the lower setae short; basal cell bare; cubital hairline absent. Speculum wide.

Legs orange-brown, with middle and hind tarsi darker. Hind coxae with a lateral crest of setae, sparse ventral and basal patches of setae, and dorsal surface bare to sparsely setose. Hind tibial spur 0.9× as long as hind basitarsus.

Propodeum from orange-brown to dark brown, often black anteriorly, with a median carina anteriorly and a costula laterally (Fig. M25); sculpture reticulate laterally above costula, rugose-reticulate below costula, smooth around spiracles. Nucha about as long as wide; apical margin slightly emarginate medially. Tuft of setae at spiracle conspicuous, with a short horizontal carina extending horizontally from spiracle to edge of propodeum.

Gaster oval, orange-brown, darker medially and anteriorly. T1 extending 0.8–0.9× length of gaster. Basal fovea with scattered setae at base. Ovipositor exserted. S1 with short, widely spaced grooves anteriorly, an irregularly alveolate medial ridge, and long grooves posteriorly (Fig. M26).

Male. Head dark brown, with metallic green reflections; ocelli red. Antennal insertions about 1 torular diameter above clypeal margin. Antennae with scape yellow-brown, flagellum mid-brown; funicular segments not nodose, with F1 slightly the longer; setae slightly shorter than segment of origin; club 1.4–1.8(1.6)× as long as F1. Malar groove complete, conspicuous.

Thorax dark red-brown, with metallic green reflections. Hind coxae with lateral and ventral pilosity and some scattered setae, but basal crest absent. Forewing faintly infumate to hyaline posterior to marginal and stigmal veins. Marginal vein 1.5–2.4(1.93)× as long as stigmal vein. Costal cell margin setose for slightly less than half its length. Basal hairline very faintly infumate, with a sparse strip of about 8 setae; basal cell sparsely setose; cubital row of setae present. Propodeum dark brown-black anteriorly, orange-brown posteriorly.

Gaster dark orange-brown anteriorly grading to brown-black posteriorly, almost square. T1 extending 0.95× length of gaster.

Type data. Holotype *bifasciata*: female (USNM), "12," "Australia/ Koebele," "From Dept./ Agriculture," "1968[f]/ Type," "Ophelosia/ bifasciata/ [f] type. Gir." Publication data: "Described from one female in U.S.N.M. labelled 'Australia. Koebele. From Dep. Agric. 12.' Associated with coccinellid larvae."

Holotype *viridinotata*: female (USNM), "Australia/ Koebele," "Type/ 19690/ USNM," "Ophelosia/ viridinotata/ Gir [f] type." Publication data: "Described from a female labelled 'Australia. Koebele.' *Type*: U.S.N.M., the above female."

Holotype *rousseaui*: female (QMBA), "Asaphomorphella/ rousseaui Gir/ [f] type." Publication data: "*Hab.*-South Australia: Port Lincoln (A. M. Lea)."

Material examined. Type specimens, plus 47 non-type examples (20 females, 27 males; NZAC). **ND.** Kerikeri, 5 Mar 1991, JGC, ex *Pseudococcus longispinus* mummy on persimmon, 3 females. **AK.** Mt Albert, MARC, 5 Apr 1991, JGC, 2 females, 1 ex *Anagyrus fusciventris* (Encyrtidae) in *Pseudococcus longispinus* on persimmon, 1 ex *P. calceolariae* mummy on persimmon. Glenfield, 21 Nov 1990, D. Steven, ex *P. longispinus*, 2 males. Glenfield, 27 Apr 1987, D. Steven, on desk, 1 female. Takapuna, 22 Apr 1966, P.S. Crowhurst 1208, ex *Nipaecoccus aurilanatus* on *Araucaria excelsa*, 13 females, 26 males. Auckland, Alison Park, 15 Feb 1966, P.S. Crowhurst, ex *Nipaecoccus aurilanatus* on *Araucaria excelsa,* 2 females. **WO.** Ohinewai, 5 Apr 1991, D. Steven, ex *Pseudococcus longispinus* mummy, 1 male. **BP.** Edgecumbe, 14 Apr 1990, JGC, reared ex *Pseudococcus longispinus* mummies from willow shelter in kiwifruit orchard, 1 female. **GB.** Matawhero, 30 Jul 1989, JGC, ex *Pseudococcus sp.* on grapevine, 1 female. Manutuke, Opou vineyards, 31 May 1983, JGC, ex *P. calceolariae*, 1 female. Gisborne, 8 Aug 1989, JGC, ex *Pseudococcus* sp., 1 male. Ormond, 27 Feb 1991, JGC, ex *Pseudococcus* mummies on grapefruit, 2 females. **HB.** Havelock Nth Research Orchard, 31 May

1983, JGC, from mealybugs on apples, Opou Band 3, *P. calceolariae*, 1 female. Havelock Nth, 23 Apr 1991, JGC, ex *Pseudococcus calceolariae* ovisac, 1 female. Havelock Nth, 24 Apr 1991, JGC, ex *Pseudococcus* mummy, 1 male.
AK, WO, BP, GB, HB / —.

Also examples from Papua New Guinea (4 females, BPBM) and Australia (185 females, 63 males, mostly ANIC).

Distribution. Papua New Guinea and Australia (W. Australia, S. Australia, Queensland, N.S.W., A.C.T), as well as New Zealand.

Biology. Reared from *Pseudococcus calceolariae* (incl. mummies on persimmon, and ovisacs); *P. longispinus* (incl. mummies from *Salix* shelter in kiwifruit orchard); hyperparasitic on *Anagyrus fusciventris* in *P. longispinus*; *Planococcus citri*; *Nipaecoccus aurilanatus* on *Araucaria excelsa*; *Pseudoripersia turgipes* mummies on *Casuarina cunninghami*; ex mealybug mummies; ex *Parapriasus australiasiae*; *Eriosoma lanigerum* on apple; woolly coccid complex, free in sac; collected as pupae from woolly mass surrounding mealybugs infesting *Myoporum insulare*; hyperparasitoid of Lepidoptera; ex coccinellid host; and ?*Acacia* fruit galls.

These records document *O. bifasciata* as a pseudococcid egg predator and a primary parasitoid of pseudococcids. The species has also been reared from Aphidiidae, presumably as a hyperparasitoid, and as a hyperparasitoid of *P. longispinus* via an encyrtid. There are two records, one as a hyperparasitoid via a lepidopteran and one as a coleopteran parasitoid, that I consider to be unreliable; along with the record from *Acacia* fruit galls.

Remarks. *Ophelosia bifasciata* is diagnosed by the thick setal tuft on the forewing, with upper setae as long as proximal submarginal setae.

Girault designated type specimens labelled *Ophelosia keatsi regis*, *Ophelosia bifasciata infausta*, and *Ophelosia hypatia multiseta*, but no publications have been found containing these names. All specimens are deposited in QMBA, and are indistinguishable from *O. bifasciata*. Except in the specimen labelled *O. keatsi regis*, the ventral line of setae in the costal cell of the female forewing is broadly interrupted. However, since there is a gradient within *O. bifasciata* from a complete ventral setal line through narrowly interrupted to broadly interrupted, without any other characters consistently varying, I can see no reason to designate any separate species. Details of the Girault specimens are given below.

Ophelosia bifasciata infausta Girault: QMBA, on card "Ophelosia [f]/ bifasciata infausta/ Gir. Type [and under]

Window, Indoroopilly/ 10 Oct. 1929," "ON LOAN FROM/ QUEENSLAND MUSEUM/ BRISBANE," and on slide "Ophelosia bifasciata [f]/ infausta Gir., Type/ Indoroopilly, window x.10.1929" and a label for *Ophelosia aligherini.*

Ophelosia hypatia multiseta Girault: QMBA, on card "Ophelosia [f]/ hypatia multiseta/ Gir. Type," "QUEENSLAND/ MUSEUM" and on slide "Ophelosia [f]/ hypatia multiseta/ Gir. Type./ (inner)."

Ophelosia keatsi regis Girault (1927: 334): QMBA, on card "Ophelosia [f]/ keatsi Gir. regis/ Gir. Type [and underneath] Indoroopilly 1933/ window, 8 July," "ON LOAN FROM/ QUEENSLAND MUSEUM/ BRISBANE," and on slide "Ophelosia keatsi Gir. [f]/ regis Gir. Type/ (inner)," "Ophelosia/ ex tag/ Ipswich/ 26 Oct. 1919." Slide with 2 coverslips, the larger containing the head with both antennae (one whole and one missing club), 2 forewings, 1 hind wing, 2 hind legs (one without coxa), and 1 foreleg with pronotum attached.

Ophelosia charlesi new species

Fig. 4, 17, 26, 27, M27–30; Map 13

Female (Fig. 4). Head orange-brown, with metallic green-blue reflections on vertex; dorsal margin moderately concave. Face 1.3–1.6(1.48)× broader than long. Occipital carina strong; ocelli removed from margin by 0.1 OD. Back of head imbricate. OD less than or equal to OOL. Eyes minutely hairy. Vertex transversely striate to rugose, with scattered long setae.

Antennal insertions less than 1 torular diameter above clypeal margin; scrobes weakly carinate dorsally, smooth. Antennae with scape and pedicel orange-brown, flagellum and club unicolorous dark brown; F1 slightly broader than long, F2 and F3 subsquare, F4 and F5 slightly broader than long; setae shorter than segment of origin; club 0.6–0.8(0.74)× as long as funicle. Genae smooth; genal carina moderately wide, not striate. Malar groove complete but weak; malar space 0.6× long axis of eye. Clypeus slightly produced. Oral margin concave between toruli, sloping down to weakly offset genal carina. Mandible with a pointed lower tooth and 2 blunt subequal upper teeth.

Thorax pale orange-brown, without metallic reflections. Pronotum imbricate, with short regular setae and a ring of about 14 pale setae not much longer than regular setation. Mesoscutum imbricate, with short regular pilosity and a pair of long setae posteriorly. Scapulae matt, with scattered setae and 2 pairs of long setae. Scutellum as long as wide, slightly convex in lateral aspect, alutaceous; setae long, dark. Frenal area delimited only by a change in sculpture to smooth and shining. Axillae with purple-blue metallic reflections, smooth except for a few longitudinal striations anterolaterally, and with a pair of long setae. Mesepisternum with a triangular depression; mesepimeron glabrous. Dorsellum mainly smooth, declivous; fovea alveolate. Metanotum smooth, with furrow coarsely striate.

Forewing (Fig. 26) with a diffuse infumate patch posterior to stigmal vein; basal hairline infumate. Marginal vein 2.2–3.3(2.69)× as long as stigmal vein. Stigmal area setose. Postmarginal vein subequal in length to stigmal vein. Costal cell with 2–6 setae on margin anterior to marginal vein; ventral row of setae uninterrupted. Basal hairline with a strip of setae about 4 wide; basal cell bare, not margined by cubital row of setae. Speculum wide.

Legs yellow-brown; middle and hind tibiae darker dorsally. Hind tibial spur 0.8× as long as hind basitarsus. Hind coxae with a lateral, a basal, and a small dorsal setal crest.

Propodeum dark orange-brown to dark brown anteriorly; nucha orange-brown. Median carina present anteriorly; costula present laterally. Sculpture reticulate anterior to costula, alveolate-rugose anteriorly, smooth around spiracles (Fig. M27). Nucha as long as wide; hind margin emarginate. Spiracle with a longitudinal carina.

Gaster medium brown, darker anteriorly, mediolaterally, and posteriorly. T1 extending 0.9× length of gaster. Basal fovea with numerous setae, not in a compact tuft. Ovipositor not extended past end of gaster. S1 with moderately spaced long grooves interrupted medially by a smooth horizontal ridge; anterior margin concave (Fig. M30).

Male. Head dark brown, with metallic green lustre. Malar groove more conspicuous than in female. Antennal insertions about 1 torular diameter above clypeal margin. Antennae (Fig. 17) with scape yellow, pedicel and flagellum medium brown. F1 the longest funicular segment; F2 to F4 decreasing in length; setae shorter than width of segment of origin; club 1.6–2.0(1.78)× as long as F1.

Thorax medium brown to dark brown, with metallic green reflections. Forewing (Fig. 27) hyaline except for infumate basal hairline. Marginal vein 1.8–2.9(2.31)× as long as stigmal vein. Costal cell margined with setae along distal half. Basal hairline with a line of setae, pigmented; basal cell with scattered setae, margined by cubital row of setae. Speculum very narrow. Hind coxae with sparse dorsal, lateral, and basal crests.

Propodeum variable in sculpture (Fig. M28, M29).

Gaster subquadrate, from medium brown anteriorly to dark brown posteriorly.

Type data. Holotype (ANIC): female, "Australia/ Loxton, S.A./ J. Altmann/ 1989," "ex laboratory/ culture/ Pseudococcus/ citrophilus."

Paratypes (9 females, 16 males; ANIC), Australia: 5 females, 11 males, S.A., Loxton, Solora orchards, 19 Feb 1992, J.A. Berry, from *Pseudococcus calceolariae* ovisacs on grapefruit, reared at Black Mtn Laboratories, A.C.T., Feb–Jun 1992 (32.48 116.28); 3 females, 5 males, Loxton, 1989, J. Altmann, ex *P. calceolariae* culture; 1 female, 35.35 149.00, A.C.T., Honeysuckle Creek, 11–22 Apr 1985, IDN & JCC, Malaise/ethanol; 2 females, 1 male, 41.50 146.03, Tas., Pelion Hut, 3 km S Mt Oakleigh, closed forest (W.E.B.S), Malaise, females 11 Feb – 1 Mar 1990, male 8 Jan – 12 Feb 1991.

Material examined. Type series, plus 411 non-type examples (262 females, 149 males; NZAC unless otherwise noted) from New Zealand. **ND.** Tangihua Range, Horokaka, 6 Apr 1993, R.C. Henderson, reared from ovisac of *Paraferrisia podocarpi* on *Dacrydium cupressinum,* 1 female. Kerikeri, 5–6 Mar 1991, JGC, 2 females ex *P. calceolariae* ovisac, 6 females, 3 males. **AK.** Huia, Sep 1980, CFB, ex *Paraferrisia podocarpi* on *Dacrycarpus dacrydioides,* 1 female, 1 male. Whatipu, 25 Feb 1979, L.A. Mound, 2 males. Reared series from MARC, Mt Albert (originally collected in HB), May–Oct 1990, J.A. Berry, ex *Pseudococcus calceolariae* culture, 83 females, 71 males. Titirangi, Oct 1980, G.W. Ramsay, Malaise trap in garden, 1 female, 1 male. Waitakere Range, Sep–Nov 1990, JSN, 5 females. Massey, EWV, Malaise trap, 27 Sep 1979, 17 Jun 1979, 24 Jul 1980, 16 Aug 1980, 4 females. **WO.** Waitomo Caves, 24 Mar 1991, D. Steven, 2 females. Ohaupo, McFall Rd, 4 Apr 1990, JGC, ex *Pseudococcus calceolariae* ovisac, 1 female, 6 males. **BP.** Tauranga, Welcome Bay, 5 Apr 1991, D. Steven, ex *Pseudococcus* mummy, 1 male. Edgecumbe, 30 Jun 1989, JGC, ex *Pseudococcus longispinus* on *Salix,* 1 female. **GB.** Manutuke, 30 Jul 1989, JGC, from *Pseudococcus*-infested bark of grapevine, 1 female. Manutuke, 2 Aug 1989, JGC, ex *Pseudococcus* sp. from grapevine, 1 male. Manutuke, Opou vineyards, 31 Mar 1983, ex *Pseudococcus calceolariae* on apples, 3 females, 4 males. Manutuke, Opou vineyards, 31 May 1983, ex *P. calceolariae* on apples, 8 females, 1 male. Manutuke, 8 Aug 1990, JGC, ex *Pseudococcus* mummies on citrus, 3 males. Opou vineyards, 23–28 Sep 1982, ex *Pseudococcus* egg batches, 3 females, 3 males. Gisborne, 27 Feb 1991, JGC, ex *Pseudococcus calceolariae* (one from a mummy) on citrus, 4 males. Patutahi, 28 Feb 1991, JGC, ex *Pseudococcus calceolariae* ovisac, 1 female, 1 male. Ormond, 27 Feb 1991, JGC, on navel orange property, 2 females. Gisborne, 3 May 1961, ex *Pseudococcus longispinus* on lemon, 3 males. **HB.** Havelock North Research Orchard, 3 Nov 1982, JGC, from mealybugs in corrugated bands on apple trunks, 19 females, 17 males. Havelock North Research Orchard, 12 Jan 1983, JGC, ex *Pseudococcus calceolariae* egg batch, 1 female, 2 males. Havelock North Research Orchard, Jan 1981, JGC, ex *Pseudococcus obscurus* egg sac, 1 male. HNRO, 15 Dec 1982, JGC, ex *Pseudococcus calceolariae,* 86 females, 8 males. Havelock North Research Orchard, 15 Dec 1982, ex *Pseudococcus obscurus,* 1 male. Havelock North Research Orchard, JGC, from mealybugs on apples: 3 Nov 1982 (5 females, 14 males), 24 Nov 1982 (2 , 1), 15 Dec 1982 (15, 16), 3 Feb 1983 (26, 31), 9 Mar 1983 (69, 104), 30 Mar 1983 (5, 4), 2 May 1983 (7, 8) (hosts: *Pseudococcus calceolariae* 34 records from males, one specifying eggsacs, and 31 records from females, one specifying eggsacs; *Pseudococcus affinis* 98 records from males, one specifying 2nd instar; 66 records from females). Havelock Nth, 23–24 Apr 1991, JGC, 4 females, 1 male (2 females ex *Pseudococcus affinis* ovisac, and 2 ex *Ps. calceolariae* ovisac). Hastings, 23 Apr 1991, JGC, ex *Pseudococcus affinis* ovisac, 3 females, 2 males. **SD.** Shakespeare Bay, 11 Aug 1969, G. Kuschel, litter 69/147, 1 male, 1 female. Kenepuru Sd, foot Mt Stokes, 10 Oct 1967, J.I. Townsend, beating, 1 female. **NN.** Farewell Spit, 4 Dec 1980, JSN, EWV, AKW, 1 female. Kaihoka Lakes, 4 Dec 1980, coastal forest, JSN, EVW, AKW, 7 females, 1 male. Eves Valley, 8 Dec 1980, JSN, AKW, EWV, 2 females. Totaranui, 600 m, 5 Dec 1980, JSN, EWV, AKW, 2 females. Wakefield, 7 Jan 1964, EWV, ex mealybug egg sac on *Dacrydium colensoi,* 2 females. Appleby Research Orchard, Jun 1963, EWV, feeding on eggs of *Phenacoccus graminicola,* 4 females, 6 males. Nelson, Feb–Mar 1925, 14 Oct 1926, 6 Mar 1927, 19 Mar 1927, 26 Mar 1927, 12 May 1928, long series of males and females. Riwaka, 31 Aug 1965, JAdB, ex *Pseudococcus* sp., 1 female, 4 males. Pelorus Bridge, 28 Mar 1966, DBR, ex mealybug eggsac on *Leptospermum [Kunzea] ericoides,* 2 females. **BR.** Mt Robert, 600–1400 m, 10 Dec 1980, JSN, EWV, AKW, *Nothofagus* forest and grass, 2 males. **KA.** Oaro (LUNZ): 18 Mar 1978, 1 female; 21 Mar 1982, JWE, 1 female. **MC.** Christchurch, Dallington, 27 Jun 1920, ESG, 1 female.

The following specimens differ in having more setae on the costal wing margin (up to 11) and less on the basal hairline, a metallic tinge to the thorax, and a darker propodeum. **ND.** Waipoua S.F., along Waipoua Stm, 70 m, 16–21 Mar 1978, S. & J. Peck, Malaise trap, 1 female. Omahutu S.F., 6 Oct 1980, JSN, 1 female. **AK.** Birkenhead, Sep 1980, JFL, Malaise trap, 1 female. **CL.** Kauaeranga Vly, 1 Feb 1981, JSN, 1 female. Little Barrier I., 10 Mar 1974, JSD, *Nothofagus/Agathis* forest, 1 female. **SD.** Pelorus Bridge, 13 Dec 1980, JSN, EWV, AKW, *Podocarpus* forest, 1 female. Ship Cove, 27–30 Nov 1972, GK, ??. **NN.** Golden Bay, 25 May 1960, ex *Trionymus podocarpi* egg sac on *Podocarpus dacrydioides,* 1 female, 2 males. Upper Takaka R., Asbestos Mine Tr., 700 m, 2

Dec 1980, mixed *Nothofagus* forest, JSN, EWV, AKW, 1 female. Wairoa Gorge, Garden Vly, 24 Sep 1964, J.I. Townsend, from litter, 1 female. Wakefield, Regents Park, 26 Jan 1965, EWV, ex mealybug on *Dacrydium colensoi*, 1 female. Wakefield, 30 Aug 1967, JSD, 1 female. Nelson, Nov 1924, ESG, 1 female, 1 male. Maitai Vly, 26 Jan 1968, JAdeB, ex mealybug on *Fuchsia excorticata*, 1 female. **MB.** 1 female, Onamalutu, 4 Sep 1966, E. Collyer, ex mealybug eggsac on *Podocarpus dacrydioides*. **BR.** L. Rotoroa, 11 Dec 1981, JSN, EWV, AKW, 1 female. Capleston Beetle Res., Redmans Creek, 245 m, litter, 1 female. **SI.** Thule, 7 Feb 1968, EWV, ex mealybug on *Dacrydium cupressinum*, 1 female.

A group of specimens from Australia differ in the sculpture of S1 and in having a broader tuft on the forewing.

ND, AK, WO, CL, BP, GB, HB / SD, NN, BR, MB, KA, MC / SI.

Biology. Reared from ovisac of *Trionymus (=Paraferrisia) podocarpi* on *Dacrydium cupressinum* and *Dacrycarpus dacrydioides*, and *Trionymus podocarpi* eggsac on *Dacrycarpus dacrydioides*; mealybugs on *Malus sylvestris*; mealybug on *Lagarostrobos colensoi*; mealybug on *Dacrydium cupressinum*; mealybug eggsac on *Lagarostrobos colensoi*; mealybug eggsac on *Dacrycarpus dacrydioides*; ex mealybug eggsac on *Fuchsia excorticata*; mealybug eggsac on *Kunzea ericoides*; feeding on eggs of *Phenacoccus graminosus* (=*graminicola*); *Pseudococcus*-infested bark of *Vitis vinifera*; *P. longispinus*; *P. longispinus* on *Salix*; *P. longispinus* (=*P. adonidum*) on *Citrus limon*; *Pseudococcus calceolariae* (=*P. citrophilus*) culture; reared from *P. calceolariae* ovisacs on grapefruit; *P. calceolariae* eggsacs on *Malus sylvestris*; *P. calceolariae* on *Vitis vinifera*; *P. calceolariae* on citrus; *Pseudococcus affinis* (=*P. obscurus*); *P. affinis* egg sac; *P. affinis* 2nd instar on *Malus sylvestris*.

Most detailed rearing data record *O. charlesi* as a gregarious egg predator. The only exceptions are seven males from New Zealand (WO, BP, GB, HB) on card tags in the NZAC along with their mummified host remains (all *Pseudococcus* sp.); and data from J.G. Charles (pers. comm.) which records *O. charlesi* as a primary parasitoid of young third-instar *P. longispinus* and *P. calceolariae*.

Life history data were recorded for *O. charlesi* as follows. Mean time between introduction of adult female and male wasps to host and emergence of offspring at ambient laboratory temperature 51.92 days (n = 53, sd = 4.41); mean for males 51.69 days (n = 29, sd = 4.32); mean for females 52.21 days (n = 24, sd = 4.6). Longest period recorded for adult female survival in laboratory 56 days.

Distribution. Australia (S. Australia, N.S.W., A.C.T.) and New Zealand.

Remarks. *Ophelosia charlesi* and *O. leai* (Australia) are diagnosed by the distinctive setosity of the forewing. *O. charlesii* is differentiated by the relatively bare basal cell and the relative lack of pilosity on the apex of the costal cell margin of both sexes, and the first funicular segment of the male being considerably shorter than the scape.

O. charlesi is named for Mr John Charles (Hort Research NZ Ltd), who did much of the collecting and rearing. A relatively small group of specimens have been selected as paratypes because of the variation noted in the material examined. Since *O. charlesi* is presumed to be endemic to Australia, paratypes have been selected from that country, excluding specimens noted to differ in forewing and S1 character states.

Ophelosia crawfordi Riley

Fig. 18, M31, M32; Map 14

crawfordi Riley, 1890: 249–250 (*Ophelosia*). Girault 1916: 227. Wilson 1963: 4, 9. Smith & Compere 1931: 1109. Charles 1989: 226–227, 234. Bouček 1988a: 354, fig. 650.
sulcata Girault, 1925b: 1 (*Ophelosia*). Dahms 1986: 571–572. Bouček 1988a: 54. New synonymy.

Female. Head orange-brown, without metallic lustre; dorsal margin moderately convex. Face 1.5–1.9(1.61)× broader than long. Occipital carina strong; back of head alutaceous. Ocelli about 0.2× OD from occipital carina; OD subequal to OOL. Eyes minutely hairy. Vertex and face transversely rugose, with scattered long setae.

Antennal insertions well below eye level, less than 1 torular diameter above clypeal margin; scrobes weakly transversly rugose laterally, smooth medially, delimited anteriorly by a weak carina, or not at all (Fig. M31). Antennae with scape and funicle yellow, pedicel darker, and club grading to medium brown apically; F1 to F3 square, F4 and F5 slightly broader than long; club 0.7–0.9(0.86)× as long as funicle. Malar groove complete but inconspicuous; malar space 0.6× long axis of eye. Lower face and genae striate; genal carina wide, not striate. Clypeus slightly produced. Oral margin between toruli straight, sloping to very slightly offset genal carina (Fig. M31). Mandibles reduced, with 2 very blunt, equal teeth.

Thorax pale orange-brown, without metallic reflections. Pronotum only slightly narrower than mesoscutum, with regular short pilosity over entire surface and a ring of 10 setae, sculptured anterior to ring, smooth and shiny posteriorly. Mesoscutum finely transversely rugose, covered in regular short pilosity, with a pair of long, dark setae at posterior edge, abutting scutellum. Scapulae transversely rugose, with regular pilosity and 2 pairs of long, dark setae. Scutellum slightly longer than wide, convex in lateral aspect, alutaceous, with a very subtle to almost nonexistent longitudinal groove medially; anterior pair of setae closer together than posterior pair. Frenal area not delimited, except at apex as a smooth strip. Axillae slightly longitudinally striate, with a pair of setae. Mesepisternum with a faintly striate depressed triangular area; mesepimeron glabrous to faintly striate transversely. Dorsellum smooth and triangular; dorsellar fovea alveolate. Metanotum smooth, with furrow striate.

Forewing darkly infumate at basal hairline and posterior to stigmal vein. Marginal vein 2.3–2.9(2.72)× as long as stigmal vein. Postmarginal vein 1.2× as long as stigmal vein. Stigmal area slightly setose. Costal cell with 2–6 setae on apical margin, a continuous ventral setal row, and a partial 2nd row. Submarginal row with 8 setae. Basal hairline with a conspicuous triangular tuft of long, dark setae slightly shorter than submarginals, about 5 setae wide at top; basal cell bare, not margined by cubital row of setae.

Legs and coxae yellow-brown; middle and hind tibiae darkened dorsally. Hind tibial spur as long as hind basitarsus or longer. Hind coxae with a sparse lateral setal crest, no dorsal crest, and some basal pilosity.

Propodeum orange-brown, slightly paler apically, dark brown to black around spiracles, with an anteromedian carina and laterally a costula. Sculpture reticulate anterior to costula, rugose-reticulate posteriorly, smooth around spiracles. Nucha longer than wide, its apex smooth; apical margin not emarginate medially. Spiracle with horizontal carina leading to setal tuft and forming an acute tooth at lateral margin.

Gaster orange-brown, darker basally and apically, and with a medial dark spot. Basal fovea with scattered setae at base. T1 extending 0.9× length of gaster. Ovipositor not projecting beyond end of gaster. S1 with moderately spaced longitudinal grooves interrupted by a horizontal ridge (Fig. M32).

Male. Head black, with metallic green lustre; OD about 2× OOL; vertex rugose.

Antennal insertions less than 1 torular diameter above clypeal margin, unicolorous yellow; scrobes transversely striate laterally, smooth medially, delimited anteriorly by a carina which is obscured by sculpture of scrobes. Antennae (Fig. 18) with funicular segments slightly longer than broad, strongly nodular, F1 slightly the longest; setae no longer than 1.5× segment of origin; sensilla not conspicuous; club 1.4–2.0(1.66)× as long as F1.

Thorax black, with metallic green lustre. Propodeum dark brown-black, grading to orange-brown at apex. Forewing hyaline. Marginal vein 2.3–2.8(2.53)× as long as stigmal vein. Costal cell with about 9 setae on apical margin; ventral row of setae continuous, with a partial 2nd row. Submarginal vein with 10 setae. Basal hairline infumate, with a single line of setae; basal cell almost bare; cubital row of setae present. Legs medium brown, darker dorsally. Hind coxae with a ventral row of setae only.

Gaster dark orange-brown, grading to dark brown apically. Fovea with sparse setae. T1 extending 0.9× length of gaster.

Type data. Syntypes of *crawfordi* (not seen): "described from four female and two male specimens reared by F. S. Crawford, at Adelaide, from specimens of *Icerya purchasi* received from S. Australia, 50 miles north of Adelaide." Girault (1916: 227) states that the types ("three females, two males on a tag, a male antenna on a slide. Catalogue No. 1510, U.S.N.M.") are deposited at the USNM.

Lectotype *sulcata*: female (QMBA) here designated, on card labelled "SYNTYPES/ T. 10000/ E.C.D. 1985," "*Ophelosia* [f]/ *sulcata* Girault/ Types," "QUEENSLAND MUSEUM", with 2 females (one intact, designated as lectotype, the other minus head and right wings) plus legs from another specimen. Also two slides, as follows. Slide 1 labelled "*Ophelosia* [fm]/ *sulcata* Gir./ Type," "SYNTYPES/ T.10000/ E.C.D. 1985," label for *Zaomommoencyrtus dayboroensis*; half coverslip with two crushed heads, fragments of antennae, and a thorax with hind coxa and femur and separated leg parts. Slide 2 labelled "*Ophelosia* [f]/ *sulcata* Gir./ Type (Inner)" and label for *Ophelosia hypatia*; one coverslip fragment, inner, with two forewings. The remaining specimens are paralectotypes. Publication details: "A male, 4 females from *Icerya purchasi*, Toowong, Q., July 26 1923, J. H. Simmonds, Department of Agriculture and Stock." These specimens have the status of syntypes.

Material examined. Syntypes of *sulcata*, plus 1 non-type female, NN, Nelson, 15 Jan 1926, Philpott.
— / NN.
Also 48 females, 11 males from Australia (mostly ANIC) and Java (USNM).

Biology. *O. crawfordi* is a predator of margarodid eggs, and has been reared from *Icerya purchasi* on lemon, *Leptospermum*, *Mimosa pigra*, and *Cassia* sp., and from *Icerya seychellarum*.

Distribution. Australia (S. Australia, N.S.W., Queensland), Java, and New Zealand.

Remarks. *Ophelosia crawfordi* is diagnosed by its sculptured antennal scrobes, and the shape of the propodeum (longer than broad). Girault (1925b) distinguished *O. sulcata* from *O. crawfordi* on the basis of a well defined medial longitudinal groove on its scutellum. However, among the specimens I have included in *O. crawfordi* there exists a range from a well defined groove, through a very faint groove, to a perturbation in the sculpture without a groove. Since there are no other consistently varying characters, I have synonymised *O. sulcata* with *O. crawfordi*.

Ophelosia keatsi Girault

Fig. 28, M33, M34; Map 15

keatsi Girault, 1927: 334 (*Ophelosia*). Dahms 1984: 738.
    Bouček 1988a: 354.
horatii Girault, 1937: 2 (*Ophelosia*). Dahms 1984: 695.
    Bouček 1988a: 354. New synonymy.

Female. Head orange-brown, with purple metallic reflections ranging to metallic green on vertex; dorsal margin moderately concave. Face 1.4–1.7(1.5)× broader than long. Occipital carina strong; back of head alutaceous. Ocelli removed from carina by 0.2 OD; OD less than or equal to OOL. Vertex alutaceous, with scattered long setae.

Antennal insertions less than half a torular diameter above clypeal margin; scrobes smooth, not carinate anteriorly. Antennae with scape orange-brown, pedicel and flagellum ranging from unicolorous orange-brown to unicolorous dark brown, or sometimes with club and possibly F5 dark brown and other segments orange brown; F1 slightly broader than long, and all other funicular segments square; club 0.7–0.9(0.81)× as long as funicle. Malar groove complete but not conspicuous; malar space 0.6× long axis of eye. Genae smooth; genal carina moderately wide, not striate. Oral margin very slightly emarginate between toruli, sloping to weakly offset genal carina. Mandible with a pointed lower tooth; upper tooth divided into 3 points, the upper two small and the lower larger and rounded.

Thorax orange-brown to dark orange-brown, with weak to strong metallic green and purple reflections. Pronotum imbricate, with regular short, pale setationand a ring of about 14 brown setae. Mesoscutum imbricate, with regular pale setation and a pair of longer setae. Scapulae imbricate. Scutellum slightly longer than broad, flat in lateral aspect, alutaceous; anterior pair of setae slightly closer together than posterior pair. Frenal area short, delimited only by a change in sculpture to smooth. Axillae smooth and shiny, dark orange-brown with metallic green reflections.

Mesepisternum with a shallow triangular depression; mesepimeron smooth. Dorsellum smooth and shiny; fovea alveolate. Metanotum smooth; furrow coarsely striate.

Forewing (Fig. 28) with basal hairline infumate and with a large, diffuse infumate patch posterior to marginal and stigmal veins. Marginal vein 2.7–4.6(3.37)× as long as stigmal vein. Stigmal area sparsely setose. Postmarginal vein subequal in length to stigmal vein. Costal cell with 2–7 setae on apical margin; ventral row of setae continuous, with a partial 2nd row. Basal hairline infumate, with a triangular strip of 10–25 setae, these shorter than the submarginal setae; basal cell bare; cubital hairline sometimes present distally. Speculum present.

Legs orange-brown; middle and hind tibiae sometimes darker dorsally. Hind tibial spur 0.7–0.9× as long as hind basitarsus. Hind coxae with a dorsal and a lateral diffuse crest of setae.

Propodeum orange-brown to dark brown-black with metallic blue reflections, with an anteromedian carina and a costula laterally. Sculpture reticulate laterally, posterior to costula, rugose-reticulate anterior to costula, smooth around spiracles. Tufts of setae under spiracles conspicuous, long. Nucha as long as broad; distal margin conspicuously excised apically.

Gaster orange-brown to dark brown-black, with or without medial and apical darkening, oval. Basal fovea with a small tuft of setae . T1 extending 0.5–0.8× length of gaster. Ovipositor exserted. S1 with moderately spaced longitudinal grooves interrupted by a smooth to alveolate medial ridge (Fig. M33, M34).

Male. Head orange-brown. Antennal insertions about 1 torular diameter above clypeal margin. Antennae with scapes yellow, remainder medium brown; F1 slightly longer than F2, and F2 to F4 subequal in length; setae and sensilla shorter than segment of origin; club 1.2–2.1(1.66)× as long as F1.

Thorax orange grading to orange-brown, with slight metallic blue-purple lustre. Hind coxae with sparse dorsal, lateral, and basal pilosity. Forewing infumate. Marginal vein 3.8–5.0(3.63)× as long as stigmal vein. Costal cell with about 8 setae along apical margin. Basal hairline with a strip of about 8 short setae, infumate; basal cell bare; cubital hairline absent.

Gaster yellow-brown grading to medium brown apically. T1 extending 0.6× length of gaster.

Type data. Holotype *keatsi*: female (SAMA) on card labelled "Hughes/ S. Australia/ A. M. Lea," "Type," "Ophelosia Type [f]/ keatsi Girault," "Ophelosia/ keatsi Gir./South Australia/TYPE," "S. A. Museum/ Specimen;"

head and right wings missing, prothorax separated. Publication details: "S. Aust.: Hughes (A. M. Lea)."

Holotype *horatii*: female (QMBA) on card labelled "HOLOTYPE/ T.9083/ E.C.D. 1983," "Ophelosia [f]/ horatii Gir/ Type [and under] Queensland/ A.A.G," "QUEENSLAND MUSEUM" (head, forewings and 1 hind wing, and some legs missing) and on slide labelled "Ophelosia [f]/horatii Gir. Type," "HOLOTYPE/T.9083/ E.C.D. 1983" (inner coverslip covering crushed head and 1 forewing); also a label for *Ophelosia semirufa* on same slide. Publication details: no specimen designated; only information "Queensland."

Material examined. Type specimens, plus 30 non-type examples (22 females, 8 males; NZAC unless otherwise noted). **BP.** L. Rotoiti Res., N Rotorua, 24–29 Mar 1978, S. & J. Peck, *Podocarpus* forest, 1 female. **GB.** Gisborne, 27 Feb 1991, JGC, reared ex *Pseudococcus* sp. on citrus, 1 female. **HB.** Hastings, 24 Apr 1991, JGC, ex *Pseudococcus affinis* on citrus, 2 females. **WI.** Palmerston North, Munro's Bush, Mar 1981, P. Watt, Malaise trap, 1 male. **NN.** Appleby Research Orchard, Jun 1963, feeding on eggs of *Phenacoccus graminosus*, 0148, 2 females, 5 males. Nelson, Saxon's Road, 14 Feb 1964, ESG, 2 females. 88 Valley, Parkes Farm, 2 Mar 1971, N.A. Martin, 1 female. **CO.** The Horn Range, 900 m, 8 Feb 1986, JWE, sweeping tussock, 1 female (LUNZ). **OL.** Coronet Pk, 1640 m, Jan 1981, tussock/alpine shrubs, *Hebe* mat plants, JSN, EWV, AKW, 1 female. **Chatham Is.** Waitangi, 24 Feb 1967, D-vac, *Juncus*, EWV, 4 females, 4 males. Mangahou, 10 Feb 1967, moss sample, AKW, EWV, 1 female, 1 male.

BP, GB, HB, WI / NN, CO, OL / Chatham Is.

Also 120 females, 9 males from Australia (mostly ANIC).

Biology. *O. keatsi* is an egg predator and possibly also a parasitoid of pseudococcids. It has been reared from *Pseudococcus longispinus* and from *P. affinis* on citrus, and found feeding on eggs of *Phenacoccus graminicola*.

Distribution. Australia (all states except Northern Territory) and New Zealand.

Remarks. *Ophelosia keatsi* is diagnosed by the lack of a carina at the anterior of the antennal scrobes, together with fully developed wings. Some specimens from Western Australia, New South Wales, and the Australian Capital Territory have the thorax metallic. There are two forms of S1 morphology (Fig. M33, M34), but no other characters vary consistently between these two groups.

Ophelosia mcglashani new species

Fig. 3, 29, M35; Map 16

Female (Fig. 3). Head orange-brown; dorsal margin weakly concave. Face 1.4–1.6(1.49)× broader than long. Occipital carina very weak. Ocelli removed from ocellar margin by 1.0× OD; OD about 0.5× OOL. Vertex very finely transversely striate, with scattered long setae.

Antennal insertions slightly less than 1 torular diameter above clypeal margin; scrobes smooth and shiny, not carinate anteriorly. Antennae with scape and pedicel orange-brown, flagellum darkening towards apex; F1 broader than long; other funicular segments square or longer than broad; club 0.8–0.9(0.88)× as long as funicle. Genae smooth; genal carina narrow, not striate. Malar groove complete, inconspicuous; malar space 0.5× long axis of eye. Clypeal margin slightly produced. Oral margin concave between toruli, sloping to offset genal carina. Mandible with pointed teeth, 1 lower and 2 upper.

Thorax dark orange-brown. Pronotum with close, regular setation and a ring of 8 setae. Mesoscutum broader than long, imbricate, with 3 pairs of setae. Scapulae imbricate. Scutellum slightly broader than long, flat in lateral aspect, engraved reticulate. Frenal area delimited only by a change in sculpture to smooth in distal third; anterior pair of setae slightly closer together than posterior pair. Axillae smooth, with several setae. Dorsellum smooth; dorsellar fovea alveolate. Mesepisternum with a shallow, alutaceous triangular depression; mesepimeron smooth and shiny. Metanotum smooth, with furrow coarsely striate.

Forewing reduced (Fig. 29), reaching slightly past propodeum, weakly infumate, darkened slightly along cubital hairline, basal hairline, and at distal end, fringed posteriorly and distally. Submarginal, marginal, and rudimentary stigmal veins present; postmarginal vein absent. Disc reduced, with at least 50 setae. Costal cell reduced, scarcely excised at apex, with 2 setae on apical margin and 7 long ventral setae overlapping costal margin. Basal hairline infumate; basal cell bare, not margined by cubital hairline.

Legs orange-brown. Hind coxae with sparse lateral, basal, and dorsal pilosity. Hind tibial spur 0.8× as long as hind basitarsus.

Propodeum dark brown anteriorly, orange-brown posteriorly, with a median carina, and laterally a costula; sculpture rugose-reticulate, smoother around spiracles. Nucha slightly broader than long, emarginate medially.

Gaster orange-brown basally grading to darker brown apically, oval. Basal fovea with scattered setae at base. T1 extending 0.9× length of gaster. Ovipositor exserted. S1 with moderately spaced long grooves interrupted medially by a wide, smooth horizontal ridge (Fig. M35).

Male. Head dark orange-brown. Antennal insertions 1 torular diameter above clypeal margin. Antennae with setation short, about as long as width of segment of origin; F1 longer than F2 to F4; club 2.2× as long as F1.

Thorax orange-brown, not metallic. Wings reduced, as in female.

Gaster rectangular, orange-brown with a dark brown band apically.

Type data. Holotype: female (NZAC), NN, "1861," "Cobb Dam/4.v.72/J. A. deBoer," "Mealybug/mature [f]/ on Chinochloa sp.," "19391."

Paratypes (11 females, 6 males; NZAC unless otherwise noted): 1 female, BR, Mt Murchison, 1220 m, 21 Nov 1971, EWV, swept cushion grass; 3 males, BR, S Victoria Range, nr Rahu Sdle, 1310 m, 27 Jan 1972, JCW, litter and moss (ANIC); 10 females (2 ANIC), 3 males, BR, Mt Robert, 15 Mar 1968, EWV.

Material examined. Type series only.
— / NN, BR.

Biology. *O. mcglashani* has been reared from a mealybug on *Chionochloa*.

Remarks. *Ophelosia mcglashani* is diagnosed by the characteristic reduced forewing, with its vestigial stigmal vein and disc with 40 or more setae. It is named for New Zealand musician Don McGlashan.

Ophelosia stenopteryx new species

Fig. 30, M36; Map 17

Female. Head orange-brown to dark brown, with faint metallic lustre; dorsal margin not concave. Face 1.3–1.4(1.36)x broader than long. Occipital carina weak; back of head alutaceous. Ocelli removed from occipital margin by more than one OD; OD 0.8× OOL. Vertex alutaceous, with scattered moderately long setae.

Antennal insertions less than 1 torular diameter above clypeal margin; scrobes smooth, not carinate anteriorly. Antennae with scape orange, pedicel and flagellum medium brown, club slightly darker; funicular segments subsquare; setae short; club 0.75× as long as funicle. Malar groove complete; malar space subequal to long axis of eye. Genae smooth; genal carina narrow, not striate. Clypeus produced, forming a long, narrow strip, its margin curved. Genal carina and clypeal margin offset. Mandibles with lower tooth pointed and upper tooth with 2 projections, the upper blunt and the lower pointed.

Thorax orange-brown. Pronotum long, about 0.3× its own width, imbricate, with regular setation and a ring of 10 setae. Mesoscutum reduced, broader than long, imbricate, with 4 pairs of setae. Notauli composed of discrete pits. Scapulae imbricate. Scutellum square, flat in lateral aspect, engraved reticulate; anterior pair of setae slightly closer together than posterior pair. Frenal area metallic green, delimited by a change in sculpture to smooth. Axillae smooth and shiny, dark orange-brown with metallic reflections. Mesepisternum with a shallow, faintly engraved reticulate triangular depression; mesepimeron smooth. Dorsellum smooth and shiny, declivous; fovea alveolate. Metanotum smooth, with furrow coarsely striate.

Forewing narrow (Fig. 30), with basal hairline infumate and with a large, diffuse infumate patch posterior to marginal and stigmal veins. Marginal vein 3.3–4.2(3.72)× as long as stigmal vein. Stigmal area bare. Postmarginal vein 1.3× as long as stigmal vein. Costal cell narrow, not excised at apex, with 3 setae on apical margin. Costal cell with ventral row of setae broadly interrupted, consisting only of a few setae at base and apex. Basal hairline infumate, with a triangular strip of 12–14 setae, these shorter than submarginal setae. Basal cell slightly setose; cubital hairline absent. Speculum wide; linea calva not delimited.

Legs orange-brown. Hind tibial spur 0.8× as long as hind basitarsus. Hind coxae with basal and sparse lateral crests of setae; dorsal crest absent.

Propodeum orange-brown to dark brown-black, with an anteromedian carina, and laterally a costula. Sculpture alveolate-reticulate except for area around spiracles and at apex of nucha. Nucha as long as broad; apical margin slightly emarginate. Tufts of setae under spiracles conspicuous, long.

Gaster orange-brown, dark brown basally and apically, oval. Basal fovea with a few setae at base, not extended down margin. T1 extending 0.6–0.8× length of gaster. Ovipositor exserted. S1 with moderately spaced longitudinal grooves interrupted medially by a wide, closely alveolate area (Fig. M36).

Male. Head dark red-brown, with metallic blue lustre.

Antennal insertions about 1.5 torular diameters above clypeal margin. Antennae with scape yellow, remainder medium brown; F1 slightly the longest funicular segment; F2 to F4 subequal in length; no flagellar segment conspicuously nodose; setae about as long as segment of origin; club 2.2–2.7(2.45)× as long as F1.

Thorax dark red-brown, with metallic blue lustre. Pronotum with a ring of 8 setae. Mesoscutum with 2 pairs of setae.

Forewing narrow, with an infumate patch and with basal hairline infumate. Marginal vein 5.0–5.2(5.1)× as long as stigmal vein. Costal cell with 2 setae along apical margin.

Basal hairline infumate, with a strip of short setae; basal cell bare; cubital hairline absent.

Gaster yellow-brown grading to medium brown apically. T1 extending 0.9× length of gaster.

Type data. Holotype: female (NZAC), "NEW ZEALAND: N.Is/ 20. mls. S. Turangi/ 19.ii.1979 L.A. Mound."

Paratypes (6 females, 2 males; NZAC unless otherwise noted): 1 female, AK, Auckland, Cornwallis Beach, Aug 1980, JSN; 2 females, WN, Otaki, 31 Jan 1957, R.A. Cumber, pasture; 1 male, NN, Cobb Dam, Mar 1981, R. Curtis, Malaise trap; 1 female, NN, Appleby, 23 Dec 1965, EWV (ANIC); 1 female, NN, Nelson, Saxon's Rd, 14 Feb 1964, ESG, rushes; 1 female, CO, Kawarau Gorge, Roaring Meg, upper powerhouse, 17 Mar 1975, JCW, moss; 1 male, CO, Watts Rock, 1200 m, Jan 1981, swept JSN, EWV.

Material examined. Type series only.

AK, TO, WN / NN, CO.

Biology. Hosts are unknown.

Remarks. *Ophelosia stenopteryx* is diagnosed by, and named for, its distinctively narrow forewings.

REFERENCES

Ashmead, W.H. 1899: Classification of the old family Chalcididae. *Proceedings of the Entomological Society of Washington 4:* 242–249.

──── 1904: Classification of the Chalcid flies or the superfamily Chalcidoidea, with descriptions of new species in the Carnegie Museum, collected in South America by Herbert H. Smith. *Memoirs of the Carnegie Museum 1(4):* i–xi, 225–551.

Ben-Dov, Y. 1993: A systematic catalogue of the soft scale insects of the world (Homoptera: Coccoidea: Coccidae). Flora and fauna handbook no. 9. Leiden, Sandhill Crane Press. 536 pp.

Berry, J.A. 1994: The systematics of the Australasian Eunotinae (Hymenoptera: Pteromalidae). Unpubl. PhD thesis, Australian National University, Canberra. xix + 433 pp.

──── (in prep.): Revision of the Moranilini (Hymenoptera: Pteromalidae: Eunotinae). *Invertebrate taxonomy.*

Bouček, Z. 1988a: Australasian Chalcidoidea, a biosystematic revision of genera of fourteen families, with a reclassification of species. Wallingford, U.K., CAB International. 832 pp.

Bouček, Z. 1988b: An overview of the classification of the Chalcidoidea (parasitic Hymenoptera). *Advances in parasitic Hymenoptera research 1988:* 11–23.

Burks, B.D. 1958: Superfamily Chalcidoidea. *In* Krombein, K. (ed.), Hymenoptera of America north of Mexico. Synoptic catalog. *Agriculture monograph 2, supplement 1:* 1–305.

──── 1978: Families Pteromalidae, Eurytomidae, Chalcididae, Leucospidae, Eucharitidae, Eupelmidae, Eulophidae, etc. *In* Krombein, K.V.; Hurd, P.D.; Smith, D.S.; Burks, B.D. *et al.*, Catalog of Hymenoptera in America north of Mexico: 1, Symphyta and Apocrita (Parasitica). Washington D.C. Pp. 768–889, 967–1043.

Cameron, P. 1883: Descriptions of new genera and species of Hymenoptera. *Transactions of the Royal Entomological Society of London 1883:* 187–197.

Charles, J.G. 1989: Pseudococcidae, mealybugs (Homoptera). Pp. 223–236 in Cameron, P.J.; Hill, R.L.; Bain, J.; Thomas, W.P. (eds), A review of biological control of invertebrate pests and weeds in New Zealand, 1874 to 1987. *CAB International Institute of Biological Control, technical communication 10.* Wallingford, U.K., CAB International. 424 pp.

──── 1993: A survey of mealybugs and their natural enemies in horticultural crops in North Island, New Zealand, with implications for biological control. *Biocontrol science and technology 3:* 405–418.

Coleman, P.J. 1980: Plate tectonics background to biogeographic development in the southwest Pacific in the last 100 million years. *Palaeogeography, palaeoclimatology, palaeoecology 31:* 105–121.

Commonwealth Institute of Entomology 1984: *Asterolecanium pustulans* (Cockerell). *Distribution maps of insect pests no. 460.*

Cox, J.M. 1987: Pseudococcidae (Insecta: Hemiptera). *Fauna of New Zealand 11.* 228 p.

Cranston, P.S.; Gullan, P.J.; Taylor, R.W. 1991: Principles and practice of systematics. Pp. 109–124 in The Insects of Australia: a textbook for students and research workers. Carlton, CSIRO / Melbourne University Press. 2 volumes, 560 + 600 pp.

Cranston, P.S.; Naumann, I.D. 1991: Biogeography. Pp. 180–197 in The Insects of Australia: a textbook for students and research workers. Carlton, CSIRO / Melbourne University Press. 2 volumes, 560 + 600 pp.

Crosby, T.K.; Dugdale, J.S.; Watt, J.C. 1976: Recording specimen localities in New Zealand: an arbitrary system of areas and codes defined. *New Zealand journal of zoology 3:* 69 + map.

Dahms, E.C. 1983: A checklist of the types of Australian Hymenoptera described by Alexandre Arsène Girault:

II. Preamble and Chalcidoidea species A–E with advisory notes. *Memoirs of the Queensland Museum 21:* 1–255.

——— 1984: A checklist of the types of Australian Hymenoptera described by Alexandre Arsène Girault: III. Chalcidoidea species F–M with advisory notes. *Memoirs of the Queensland Museum 21:* 579–842.

——— 1986: A checklist of the types of Australian Hymenoptera described by Alexandre Arsène Girault: IV. Chalcidoidea species N–Z and genera with advisory notes plus addenda and corrigenda. *Memoirs of the Queensland Museum 22:* 319–739.

Delucchi, V.; Rosen, D.; Schlinger, E.I. 1976: Relationship of systematics to biological control. Pp. 81–91 *in* C.B. Huffaker & P.S. Messenger *eds*, Theory and practice of biological control. New York, Academic Press. 788 pp.

Fleming, C.A. 1975: The geological history of New Zealand and its biota. Pp. 1–18 *in* Kuschel, G. (ed.) Biogeography and ecology in New Zealand. The Hague, Netherlands, W. Junk.

Gahan, A.B.; Peck, O. 1946: Notes on some Ashmeadian genotypes in the hymenopterous superfamily Chalcidoidea. *Journal of the Washington Academy of Science 9:* 314–317.

Gauld, I.D.; Bolton, B. (eds) 1988: The Hymenoptera. British Museum (Natural History) / O.U.P. 332 pp.

Girault, A.A. 1913: New genera and species of chalcidoid Hymenoptera in the South Australian Museum. *Transactions and proceedings of the Royal Society of South Australia 37:* 67–115.

——— 1915a: Australian Hymenoptera Chalcidoidea - VI. Supplement. *Memoirs of the Queensland Museum 3:* 313–346.

——— 1915b: Australian Hymenoptera Chalcidoidea - XI. The family Cleonymidae with descriptions of new genera and species. *Memoirs of the Queensland Museum 4:* 203–224.

——— 1916: Australian Hymenoptera Chalcidoidea. General supplement. *Memoirs of the Queensland Museum 5:* 205–230.

——— 1925a: Notes and descriptions of Australian chalcid-flies - III. (Hymenoptera). *Insecutor inscitiae menstruus 13:* 91–100.

——— 1925b: An essay on when a fly is loveable, the ceremony of baptizing some and unlovely hate. Brisbane, privately published. 4 pp.

——— 1927: Notes on and descriptions of chalcid wasps (Chalcididae) in the South Australian Museum. *Records of the South Australian Museum 3:* 309–338.

——— 1929: Notes on, and descriptions of chalcid wasps in the South Australian Museum. Concluding paper. *Transactions of the Royal Society of South Australia 53:* 309–346.

——— 1937: New naturals, unorthodoxies and non-pollutions. viz - New Hexapods. Brisbane, privately published. 3 pp.

——— 1938: Some new Australian insects which are parasites (Hym. Chalcidoidea). *Revista de entomologia (Rio de Janeiro) 8:* 80–89.

Goulet, H.; Huber, J.T. (eds) 1993: Hymenoptera of the world: an identification guide to families. Ontario, Agriculture Canada. 668 pp.

Graham, M.W.R. de V. 1969: The Pteromalidae of Northwestern Europe (Hymenoptera: Chalcidoidea). *Bulletin of the British Museum (Natural History), entomology supplement 16.* 908 p.

Grissell, E.E.; Schauff, M.E. 1990: A handbook of the families of Nearctic Chalcidoidea (Hymenoptera). Washington, D.C., The Entomological Society of Washington. 85 p.

Handlirsch, A. 1925: Überfamilie: Chalcidoidea Ashm. *In* Schroeder, Handbuch der Entomologie, vol. 3, pp. 759–772.

Harris, A.C. 1987: Pompilidae (Insecta: Hymenoptera). *Fauna of New Zealand 12.* 154 pp.

Harris, R.A. 1979: A glossary of surface sculpturing. *Californian Department of Food and Agriculture, Bureau of Entomology, occasional papers 28.* 31 p.

Heraty, J.M.; Darling, D.C. 1984: Comparative morphology of the planidial larvae of Eucharitidae and Perilampidae (Hymenoptera: Chalcidoidea). *Systematic entomology 9:* 309–328.

Howard, L.O. 1881: Report on the parasites of the Coccidae in the collection of the U.S. Department of Agriculture. *In* Comstock, United States Department of Agriculture report, 1880, pt 3, pp. 350–372.

——— 1885–86: A generic synopsis of the hymenopterous family Chalcididae. *Entomologica americana 1:* (1885) 197–199, 215–219; *2:* (1886) 33–38, 97–101.

——— 1896: On two interesting new genera of scale insect parasites. *Canadian entomologist 28:* 165–167.

Hoy, J.M. 1962: Eriococcidae (Homoptera: Coccoidea) of New Zealand. *Department of Scientific and Industrial Research bulletin 146.* 219 p.

LaSalle, J.; Boler, I. 1994: *Hadranellus anomalus* n.gen. et sp. (Hymenoptera: Eulophidae): an example of extreme intraspecific variation in an endemic New Zealand insect. *New Zealand entomologist 17:* 37–46.

Mani, M.S. 1968: Ecology and biogeography of high altitude insects. The Hague, W. Junk. 00 p.

Masi, L. 1917: Chalcididae of the Seychelles Islands. *Novitates zoologicae 24:* 121–230.

McGlone, M. 1985: Plant biogeography of New Zealand.

New Zealand journal of botany 23: 723–749.

Morales, C.F. 1989: *Saissetia oleae* (Olivier), black scale (Homoptera: Coccidae). Pp. 237–240 *in* Cameron, P.J.; Hill, R.L.; Bain,J.; Thomas, W.P. (eds), A review of biological control of invertebrate pests and weeds in New Zealand, 1874 to 1987. *CAB International Institute of Biological Control technical communication 10.* Wallingford, U.K., CAB International. 424 p.

—— 1991: Margarodidae (Insecta: Hemiptera). *Fauna of New Zealand 21.*307 p.

Morales, C.F.; Bain, J. 1989: *Icerya purchasi* Maskell, cottony cushion scale (Homoptera: Margarodidae). Pp. 207–211 *in* Cameron, P.J.; Hill, R.L.; Bain,J.; Thomas, W.P. (eds), A review of biological control of invertebrate pests and weeds in New Zealand, 1874 to 1987. *CAB International Institute of Biological Control technical communication 10.* Wallingford, U.K., CAB International. 424 p.

Naumann, I.D. 1988: Ambositrinae (Insecta: Hymenoptera: Diapriidae). *Fauna of New Zealand 15.* 165 p.

—— 1991: Hymenoptera (wasps, bees, ants, sawflies). Pp. 916–1000 *in* The Insects of Australia: a textbook for students and research workers. Carlton, CSIRO / Melbourne University Press. Two volumes, 560 + 600 pp.

Nikol'skaya, M.N. 1952: The chalcid fauna of the USSR. Israel Program for Scientific Translation, Jerusalem, 1963. 593 pp.

Noyes, J.S. 1988: Encyrtidae (Insecta: Hymenoptera). *Fauna of New Zealand 13.* 188 p.

Noyes, J.S.; Valentine, E.W. 1989a: Mymaridae (Insecta: Hymenoptera) - introduction, and review of genera. *Fauna of New Zealand 17.* 95 p.

—— 1989b: Chalcicoidea (Insecta: Hymenoptera) - introduction, and review of genera in smaller families. *Fauna of New Zealand 18.* 91 p.

Peck, O. 1963: A catalogue of the Neartic Chalcicoidea (Insecta: Hymenoptera). *Canadian Entomologist, supplement 30.* 1092 p.

Perkins, R.C.L. 1906: Notes on *Tomocera,* a genus of scale-bug parasites with description of a new species. (Hymen.). *Proceedings of the Hawaiian Entomological Society 1:* 75–76.

Poinar, G.O. 1992: Life in amber. Stanford, California, Stanford University Press.

Qin, T.K.; Gullan, P.J.; Beattie, G.A.C.; Trueman, J.W.H.; Cranston, P.S.; Fletcher, M.J.; Sands, D.P.A. (in press): The current distribution and geographical origin of the scale insect pest *Ceroplastes sinensis* Del Guercio (Hemiptera: Coccidae). *Bulletin of entomological research.*

Rasnitsyn, A.P. 1988: Paleontological succession of the Hymenopterans. *International Congress of Entomology XVIII:* 9.

Raven, P.H. 1973: Evolution of subalpine and alpine plant groups in New Zealand. *New Zealand journal of botany 11:* 177–200.

Riley, C. V. 1890: An Australian hymenopterous parasite of the fluted scale. *Insect life 2:* 248–250.

Smith, H.S.; Compere, H. 1928: A preliminary report on the insect parasites of the black scale, *Saissetia oleae* (Bernard). *University of California publications in entomology 4:* 231–334.

—— 1931: Notes on *Ophelosia crawfordi. Journal of economic entomology 24:* 1109.

Valentine, E.W. 1967: A list of the hosts of entomophagous insects of New Zealand. *New Zealand journal of science 10:* 1100–1209.

Valentine, E.W.; Walker, A.K. 1991: Annotated catalogue of New Zealand Hymenoptera. *DSIR Plant Protection report no. 4.* 84 p.

Walker, F. 1872: Notes on Chalcidiae. Part VI - Hormoceridae, Sphegigasteridae, Pteromalidae, Elasmidae, Elachistidae, Eulophidae, Entedonidae, Tetrastichidae, Trichogrammatidae. London. Pp. 89–105.

Walley, A.M.; Ross, M.I. 1991: Preliminary reconstructions for the Cretaceous to Cainozoic of the New Zealand – New Caledonia region. *Palaeogeography 31:* 1–43.

Watt, J.C. 1979: Abbreviations for entomological collections. *New Zealand journal of zoology 6:* 519–520.

Williams, D.J. 1985: Australian mealybugs. London, British Museum (Natural History). 431 p.

—— 1991: Superfamily Coccoidea. Pp. 457–464 *in* The Insects of Australia: a textbook for students and research workers. Carlton, CSIRO / Melbourne University Press. 2 volumes, 560 + 600 pp.

Williams, D.J.; Watson, G.W. 1990: The scale insects of the tropical South Pacific region. Part 3. The soft scales (Coccidae) and other families. Wallingford, U.K., C.A.B. International. 267 p.

Wilson, F. 1963: Australia as a source of beneficial insects for biological control. *Commonwealth Institute of Biological Control technical bulletin 3:* 1–28.

APPENDIX 1: Host / parasitoid associations
for Moranilini recorded in New Zealand

(a) Hosts recorded from New Zealand

APHELINIDAE (HYMENOPTERA)
Coccophagus sp. in *Eriococcus* sp.: *Aphobetus maskelli*

COCCIDAE (HEMIPTERA)
Ceroplastes sinensis (Del Guercio): *Moranila californica*
Ctenochiton sp.: *Aphobetus erroli, A. nana*
Ctenochiton elaeocarpi Maskell: *Aphobetus nana*
Ctenochiton perforatus Maskell: *Aphobetus erroli, A. nana*
Ctenochiton piperis Maskell: *Aphobetus nana*
Ctenochiton viridis Maskell: *Aphobetus maskelli, A. nana*
?Inglisia leptospermi Maskell: *Aphobetus maskelli*
Saissetia coffeae (Walker): *Moranila californica*
Saissetia oleae (Olivier): *Moranila californica*

DIASPIDIDAE (HEMIPTERA)
Leucaspis sp.: *Aphobetus maskelli, A. paucisetosus*
Leucaspis mixta de Boer: *Aphobetus nana*

ERIOCOCCIDAE (HEMIPTERA)
Eriococcus sp.: *Aphobetus cultratus, A. cyanea, A. maskelli, A. paucisetosus.*
Eriococcus elaeocarpi (Hoy): *Aphobetus paucisetosus*
Eriococcus nitidulus Hoy: *Aphobetus cyanea*

PSEUDOCOCCIDAE (HEMIPTERA)
Nipaecoccus aurilanatus (Maskell): *Aphobetus maskelli, Moranila comperei, Ophelosia bifasciata*
Paraferrisia (= Trionymus) podocarpi (Brittin): *Ophelosia charlesi*
Phenacoccus graminicola Leonardi: *Ophelosia charlesi, O. keatsi*
Pseudococcus affinis (Maskell) (= *P. obscurus* Essig): *Ophelosia charlesi, O. keatsi*
Pseudococcus calceolariae (Maskell) (= *P. citrophilus* Clausen): *Ophelosia bifasciata, O. charlesi*
Pseudococcus longispinus (Targioni-Tozzetti) (= *P. adonidum* (L.)): *Ophelosia bifasciata, O. charlesi, Aphobetus nana*

PSYLLIDAE (HEMIPTERA)
Powellia sp.: *Aphobetus maskelli*

(b) Extralimital records

The hosts and natural enemies listed below are present in New Zealand, but the associations are recorded from other areas (mainly Australia).

ALEYRODIDAE (HEMIPTERA)
Trialeurodes vaporariorum (Westwood): *Moranila comperei*

APHIDIDAE (HEMIPTERA)
Eriosoma lanigerum (Hausmann): *Ophelosia bifasciata, Moranila comperei*
Myzus persicae (Sulzer): *Moranila comperei*

BRACONIDAE (HYMENOPTERA)
Aphidius colemani Viereck (*)/*Myzus persicae* (Sulzer): *Moranila comperei*
Aphidius salicis (Haliday) / *Cavariella aegopodii* (Scopoli): *Moranila comperei*
Diaretiella rapae (McIntosh) / *Lipaphis erysimi* (Kalt): *Moranila comperei*
Ephedrus persicae Froggatt (*)/*Myzus persicae*: *Moranila comperei*

COCCIDAE (HEMIPTERA)
Ceroplastes sp.: *Moranila californica*
Coccus (= Lecanium) sp.: *Moranila californica*
Coccus hesperidum L.: *Moranila californica*
Parasaissetia nigra (Nietner): *Moranila californica*
Saissetia oleae (Olivier): *Moranila comperei*

MARGARODIDAE (HEMIPTERA)
Icerya purchasi (Maskell): *Ophelosia crawfordi*
Icerya seychellarum (Westwood)(‡): *Ophelosia crawfordi*

PSEUDOCOCCIDAE (HEMIPTERA)
Pseudococcus longispinus (Targioni-Tozzetti) (= *P. adonidum* (L.)): *Ophelosia keatsi*

---

* Present in New Zealand but occurrence unpublished (P.J. Cameron; pers. comm.).

‡ Intercepted, but not established (Morales & Bain 1989)

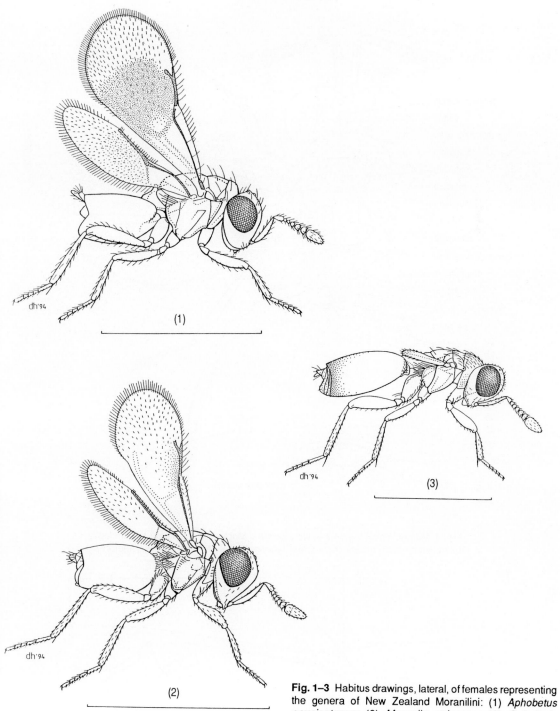

Fig. 1–3 Habitus drawings, lateral, of females representing the genera of New Zealand Moranilini: (1) *Aphobetus paucisetosus;* (2) *Moranila strigaster;* (3) *Ophelosia mcglashani.* Scale lines 0.5 mm. (Illustrator: D.W. Helmore.)

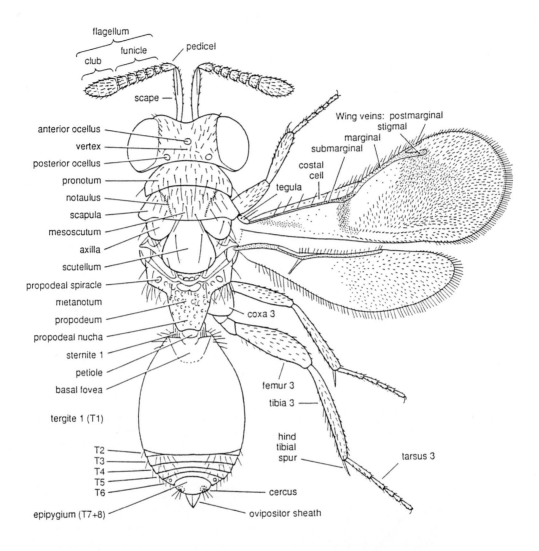

Fig. 4 Morphological features of New Zealand Moranilini, illustrating terminology used (schematic): *Ophelosia charlesi*, female, dorsal (Illustrator: D.W. Helmore).

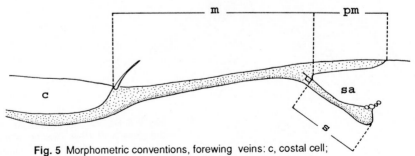

Fig. 5 Morphometric conventions, forewing veins: c, costal cell; m, marginal; pm, postmarginal; s, stigmal; sa, stigmal area.

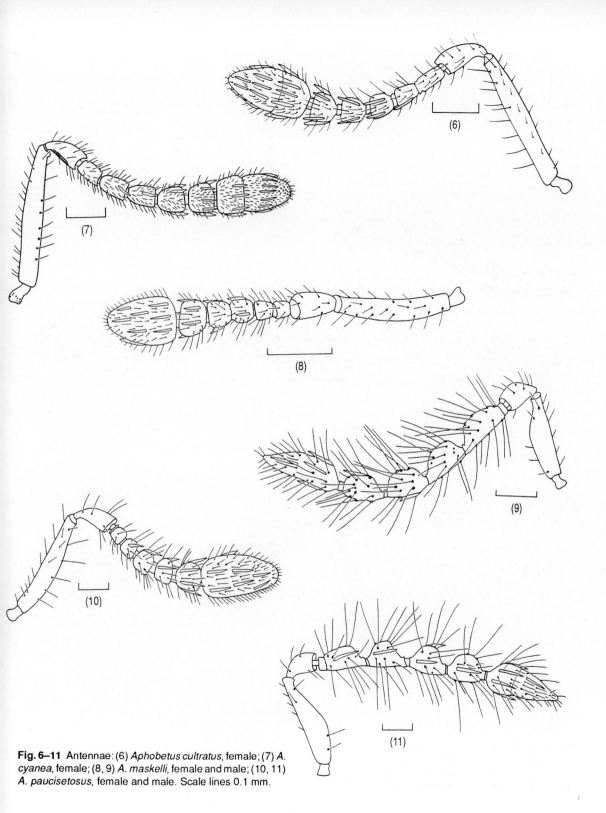

Fig. 6–11 Antennae: (6) *Aphobetus cultratus*, female; (7) *A. cyanea*, female; (8, 9) *A. maskelli*, female and male; (10, 11) *A. paucisetosus*, female and male. Scale lines 0.1 mm.

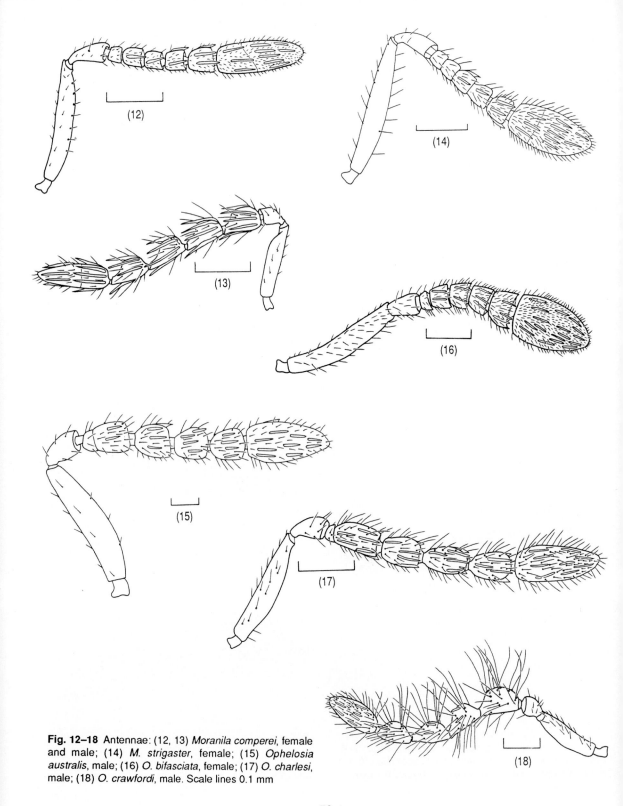

Fig. 12–18 Antennae: (12, 13) *Moranila comperei*, female and male; (14) *M. strigaster*, female; (15) *Ophelosia australis*, male; (16) *O. bifasciata*, female; (17) *O. charlesi*, male; (18) *O. crawfordi*, male. Scale lines 0.1 mm

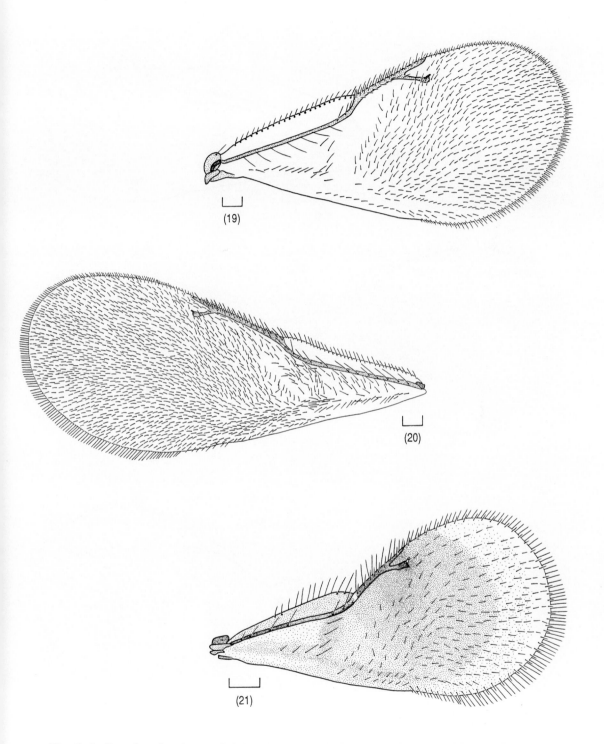

Fig. 19–21 Forewings, female: (19) *Aphobetus cultratus*; (20) *A. cyanea*; (21) *A. nana*. Scale lines 0.1 mm.

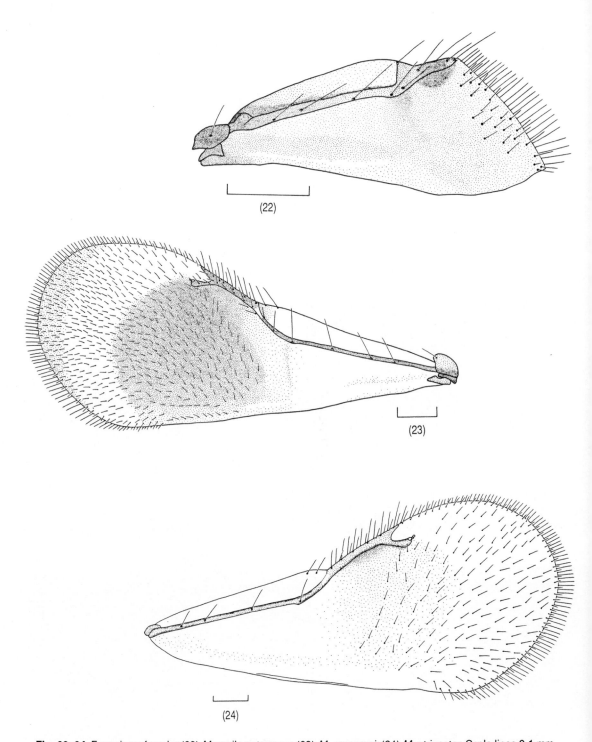

Fig. 22–24 Forewings, female: (22) *Moranila aotearoae*; (23) *M. comperei*; (24) *M. strigaster*. Scale lines 0.1 mm.

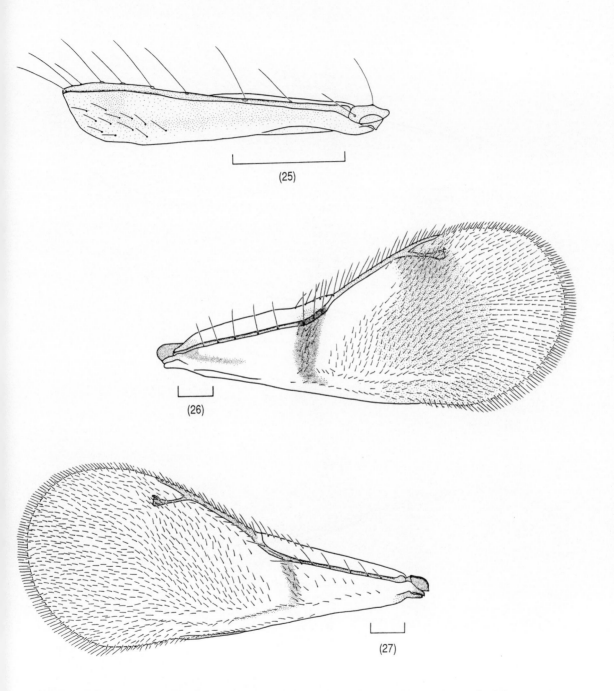

Fig. 25–27 Forewings: (25) *Ophelosia australis*, female; (26, 27) *O. charlesi*, female and male. Scale lines 0.1 mm.

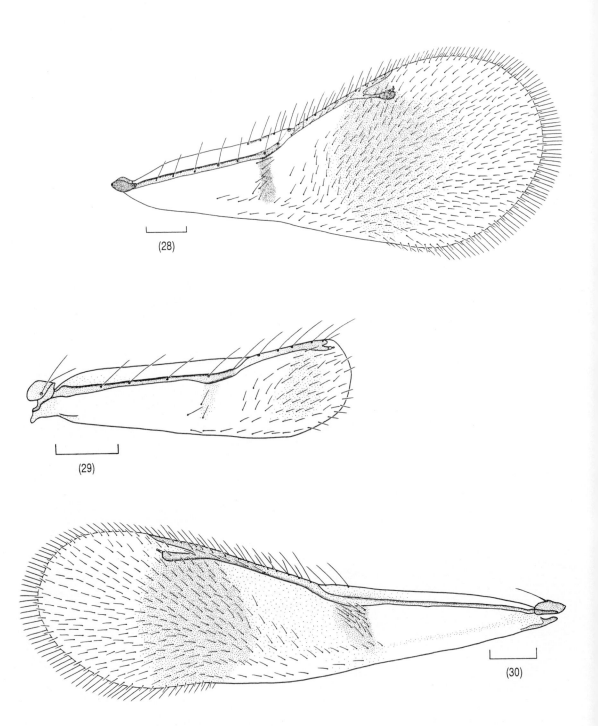

Fig. 28–30 Forewings, female: (28) *Ophelosia keatsi*; (29) *O. mcglashani*; (30) *O. stenopteryx*. Scale lines 0.1 mm.

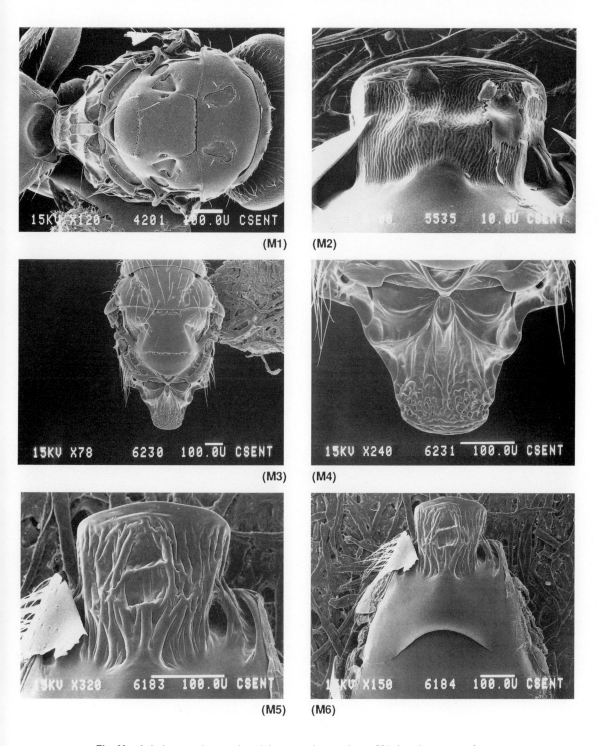

(M1) (M2)

(M3) (M4)

(M5) (M6)

Fig. M1 *Aphobetus cultratus*, dorsal thorax and propodeum; **M2** *A. cultratus*, sternite 1;
M3 *A. cyanea*, dorsal thorax and propodeum; **M4** *A. cyanea*, propodeum; **M5, 6** *A. cyanea*, sternite 1.

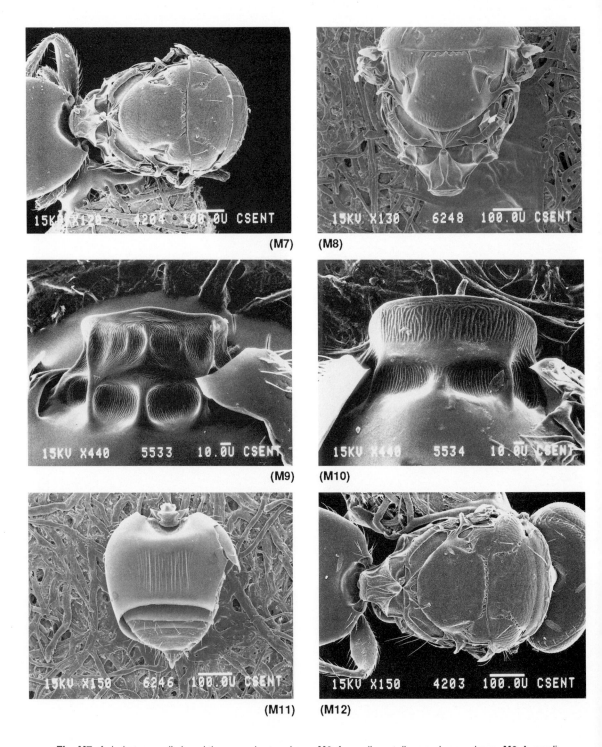

Fig. M7 *Aphobetus erroli*, dorsal thorax and propodeum; **M8** *A. erroli*, scutellum and propodeum; **M9** *A. erroli*, sternite 1; **M10** *A. maskelli*, sternite 1; **M11** *A. moundi* (Australian), tergite 1; **M12** *A. nana*, dorsal thorax.

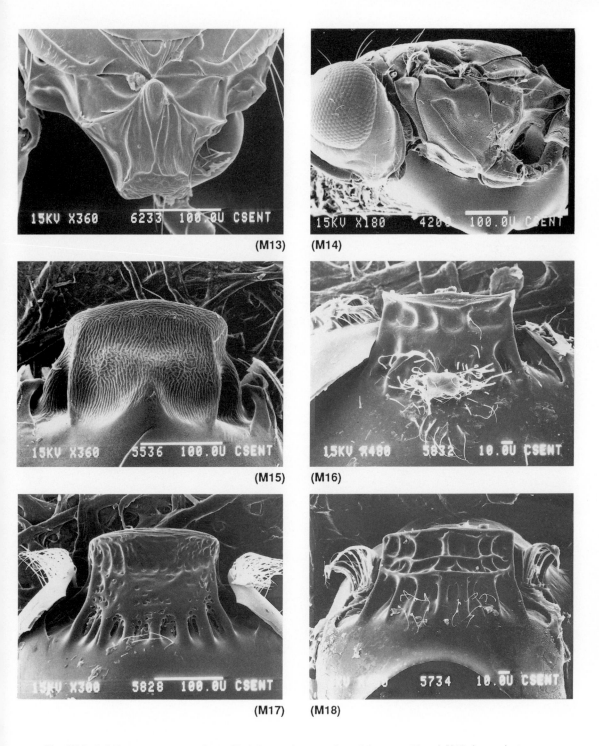

Fig. M13 *Aphobetus nana*, propodeum; **M14** *A. paucisetosus*, lateral thorax and head; **M15** *A. paucisetosus*, sternite 1; **M16** *Moranila aotearoae*, sternite 1; **M17** *M. californica*, sternite 1; **M18** *M. comperei*, sternite 1, female.

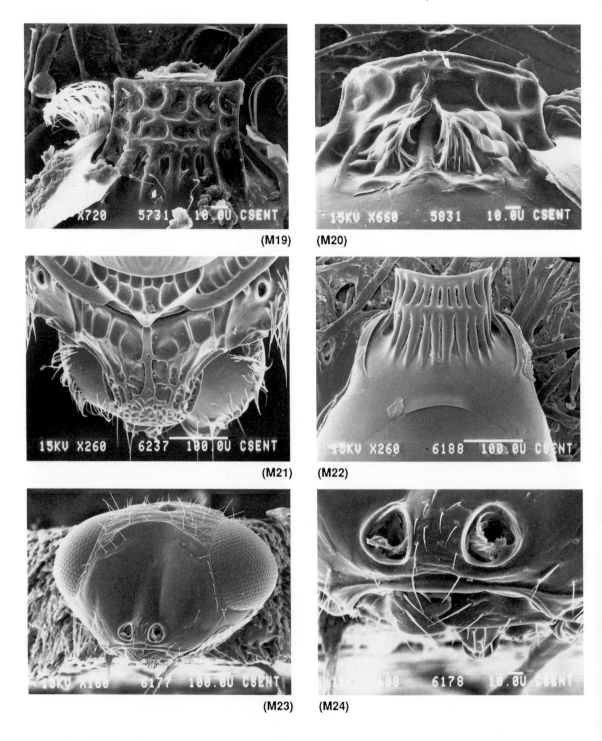

(M19)   **(M20)**

(M21)   **(M22)**

(M23)   **(M24)**

Fig. M19 *Moranila comperei*, sternite 1, male; **M20** *M. strigaster*, sternite 1; **M21** *M. viridivertex* (Australian), propodeum; **M22** *Ophelosia australis*, sternite 1; **M23** *O. bifasciata*, face, female; **M24** *O. bifasciata*, oral margin.

(M25)   (M26)

(M27)   (M28)

(M29)   (M30)

Fig. M25 *Ophelosia bifasciata*, scutellum and propodeum; **M26** *O. bifasciata*, sternite 1;
M27 *O. charlesi*, propodeum; **M28, 29** *O. charlesi*, propodeum, male (variants); **M30** *O. charlesi*, sternite 1.

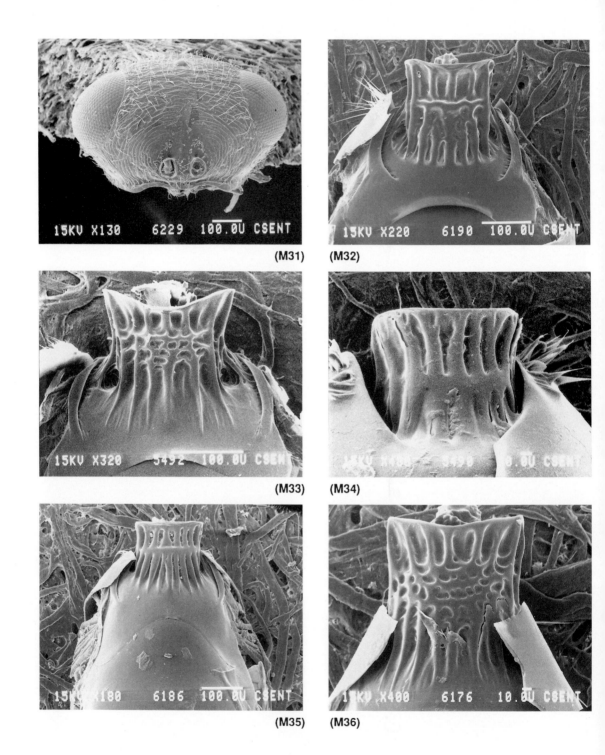

Fig. **M31** *Ophelosia crawfordi*, face, female; **M32** *O. crawfordi*, sternite 1;
M33, 34 *O. keatsi*, sternite 1; **M35** *O. mcglashani*, sternite 1; **M36** *O. stenopteryx*, sternite 1.

DISTRIBUTION MAPS

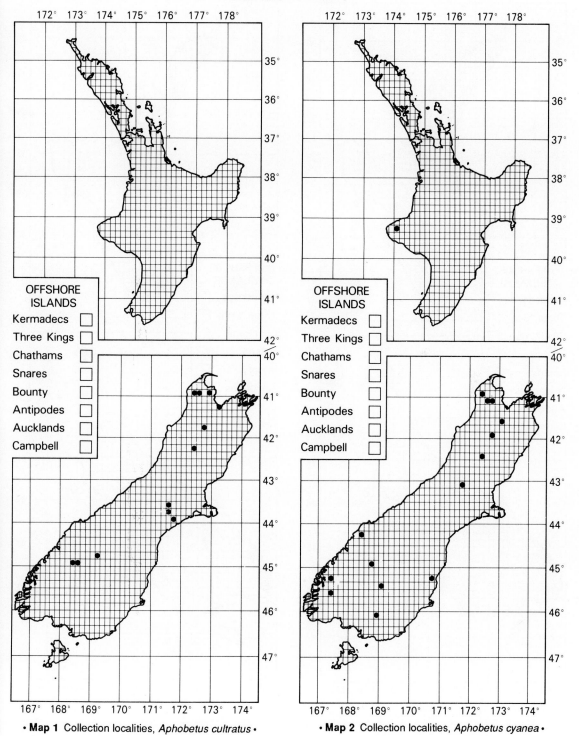

• **Map 1** Collection localities, *Aphobetus cultratus* •

• **Map 2** Collection localities, *Aphobetus cyanea* •

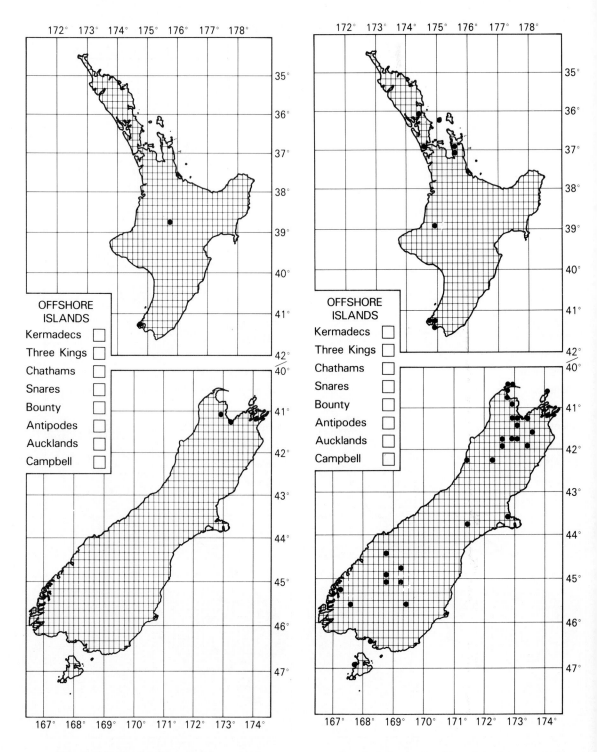

OFFSHORE
ISLANDS

Kermadecs ☐
Three Kings ☐
Chathams ☐
Snares ☐
Bounty ☐
Antipodes ☐
Aucklands ☐
Campbell ☐

• **Map 3** Collection localities, *Aphobetus erroli* •

• **Map 4** Collection localities, *Aphobetus maskelli* •

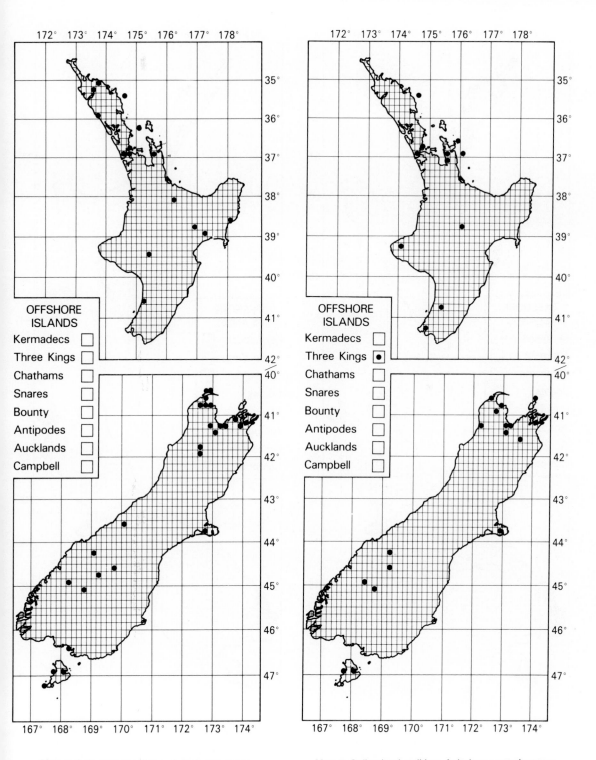

• **Map 5** Collection localities, *Aphobetus nana* •

• **Map 6** Collection localities, *Aphobetus paucisetosus* •

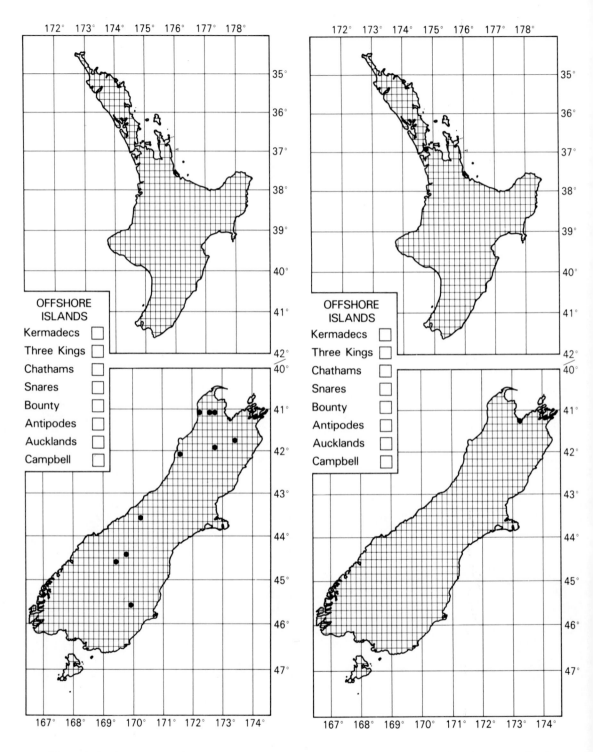

OFFSHORE
ISLANDS

Kermadecs ☐
Three Kings ☐
Chathams ☐
Snares ☐
Bounty ☐
Antipodes ☐
Aucklands ☐
Campbell ☐

OFFSHORE
ISLANDS

Kermadecs ☐
Three Kings ☐
Chathams ☐
Snares ☐
Bounty ☐
Antipodes ☐
Aucklands ☐
Campbell ☐

• **Map 7** Collection localities, *Moranila aotearoae* •

• **Map 8** Collection localities, *Moranila californica* •

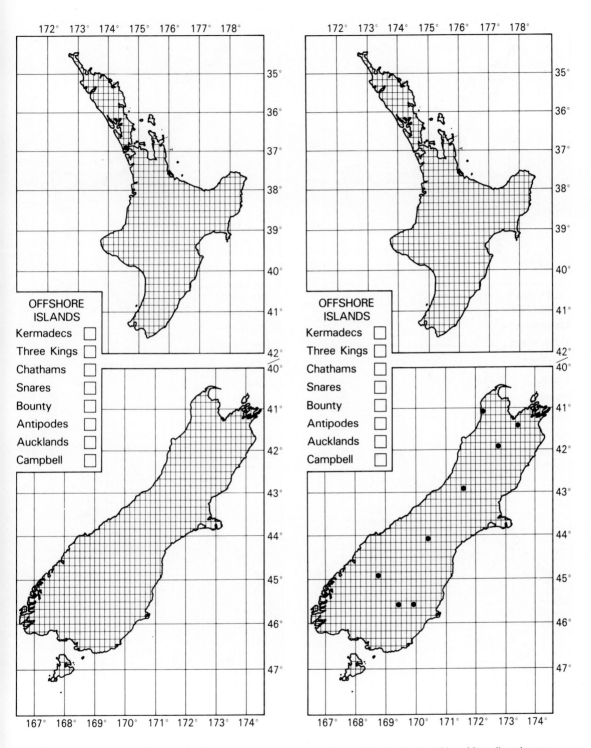

• **Map 9** Collection localities, *Moranila comperei* •

• **Map 10** Collection localities, *Moranila strigaster* •

OFFSHORE
ISLANDS

Kermadecs ☐
Three Kings ☐
Chathams ☐
Snares ☐
Bounty ☐
Antipodes ☐
Aucklands ☐
Campbell ☐

OFFSHORE
ISLANDS

Kermadecs ☐
Three Kings ☐
Chathams ☐
Snares ☐
Bounty ☐
Antipodes ☐
Aucklands ☐
Campbell ☐

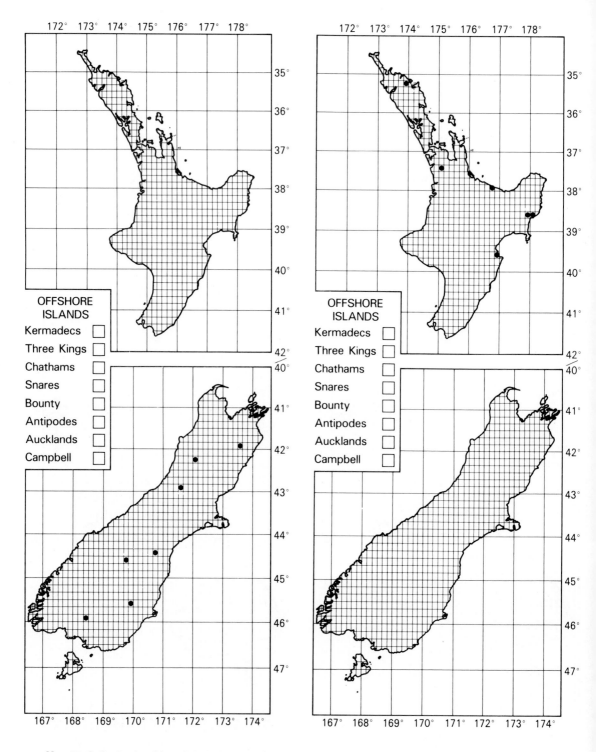

• **Map 11** Collection localities, *Ophelosia australis* •

• **Map 12** Collection localities, *Ophelosia bifasciata* •

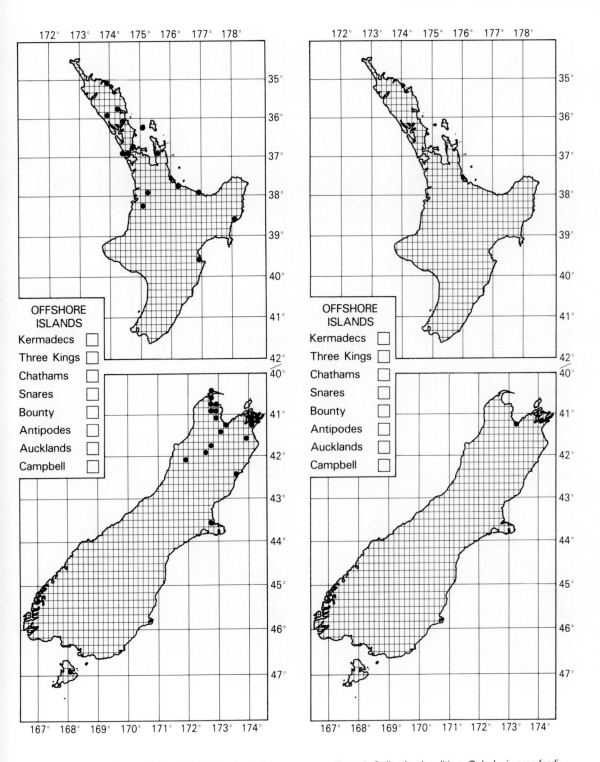

• **Map 13** Collection localities, *Ophelosia charlesi* •

• **Map 14** Collection localities, *Ophelosia crawfordi* •

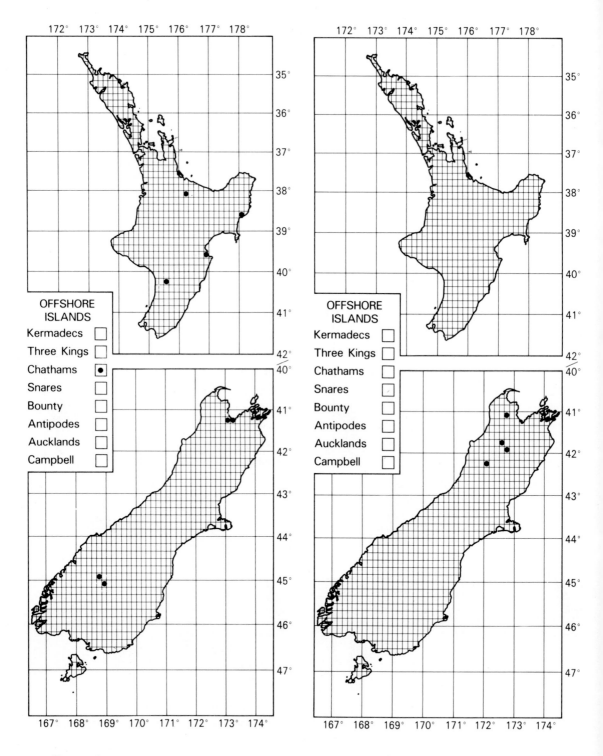

• **Map 15** Collection localities, *Ophelosia keatsi* •

• **Map 16** Collection localities, *Ophelosia mcglashani* •

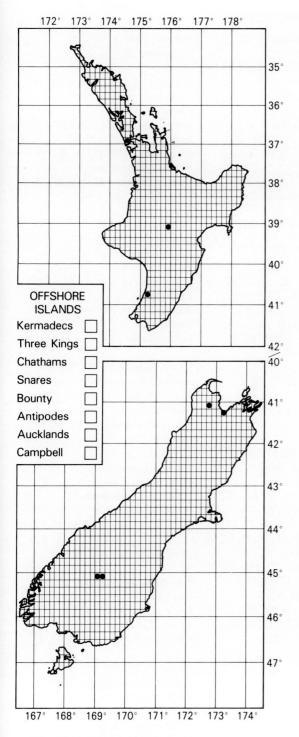

OFFSHORE
ISLANDS

Kermadecs ☐
Three Kings ☐
Chathams ☐
Snares ☐
Bounty ☐
Antipodes ☐
Aucklands ☐
Campbell ☐

• **Map 17** Collection localities, *Ophelosia stenopteryx* •

TAXONOMIC INDEX

This index covers the nominal taxa mentioned in the text, regardless of their current status in taxonomy. Page numbers in italic type denote illustrations, and in bold type a description. A suffixed letter 'k' indicates a key, and 'm' a map.

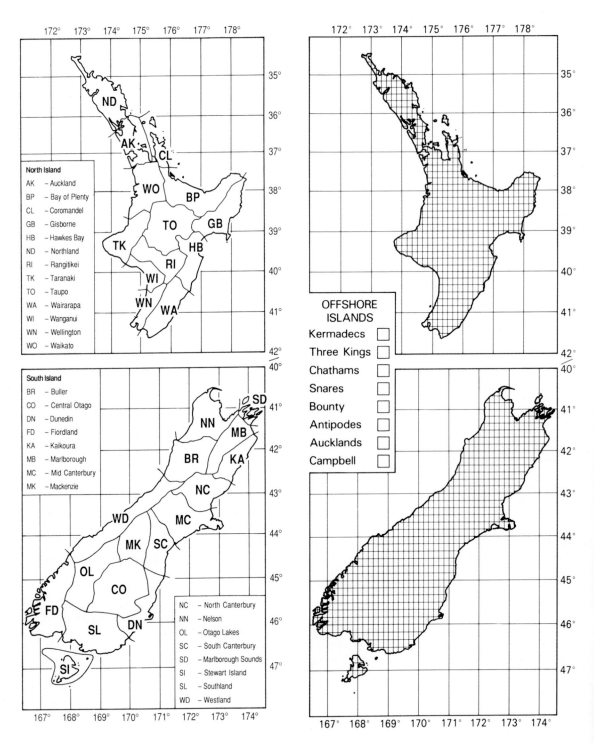

North Island

AK	– Auckland
BP	– Bay of Plenty
CL	– Coromandel
GB	– Gisborne
HB	– Hawkes Bay
ND	– Northland
RI	– Rangitikei
TK	– Taranaki
TO	– Taupo
WA	– Wairarapa
WI	– Wanganui
WN	– Wellington
WO	– Waikato

South Island

BR	– Buller
CO	– Central Otago
DN	– Dunedin
FD	– Fiordland
KA	– Kaikoura
MB	– Marlborough
MC	– Mid Canterbury
MK	– Mackenzie

NC	– North Canterbury
NN	– Nelson
OL	– Otago Lakes
SC	– South Canterbury
SD	– Marlborough Sounds
SI	– Stewart Island
SL	– Southland
WD	– Westland

OFFSHORE ISLANDS

Kermadecs ☐
Three Kings ☐
Chathams ☐
Snares ☐
Bounty ☐
Antipodes ☐
Aucklands ☐
Campbell ☐

Area codes and boundaries used to categorise specimen locality data (after Crosby *et al.* 1976)

Base-map for plotting collection localities; this may be photocopied without copyright release

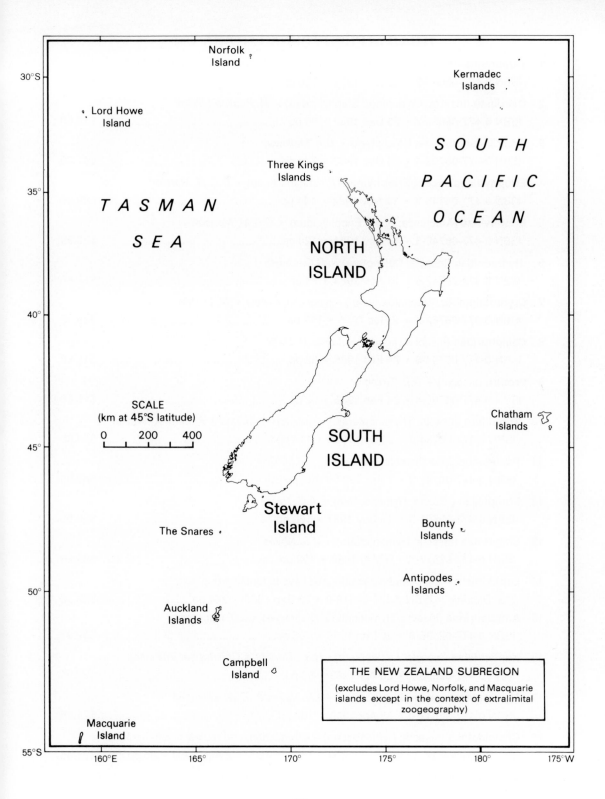

Norfolk
Island

Kermadec
Islands

Lord Howe
Island

SOUTH

PACIFIC

OCEAN

Three Kings
Islands

TASMAN

SEA

NORTH
ISLAND

Chatham
Islands

SCALE
(km at 45°S latitude)

0   200   400

SOUTH
ISLAND

Stewart
Island

Bounty
Islands

The Snares

Antipodes
Islands

Auckland
Islands

Campbell
Island

THE NEW ZEALAND SUBREGION

(excludes Lord Howe, Norfolk, and Macquarie
islands except in the context of extralimital
zoogeography)

Macquarie
Island

30°S
35°
40°
45°
50°
55°S

160°E   165°   170°   175°   180°   175°W

TITLES IN PRINT / PUNA TAITARA TAA

1 **Terebrantia** (Insecta: Thysanoptera) • *Laurence A. Mound & Annette K. Walker*
ISBN 0-477-06687-9 • 23 Dec 1982 • 120 pp. $29.95

2 **Osoriinae** (Insecta: Coleoptera: Staphylinidae) • *H. Pauline McColl*
ISBN 0-477-06688-7 • 23 Dec 1982 • 96 pp. $18.60

3 **Anthribidae** (Insecta: Coleoptera) • *B.A. Holloway*
ISBN 0-477-06703-4 • 23 Dec 1982 • 272 pp. $41.00

4 **Eriophyoidea except Eriophyinae** (Arachnida: Acari) • *D.C.M. Manson*
ISBN 0-477-06745-X • 12 Nov 1984 • 144 pp. $29.95

5 **Eriophyinae** (Arachnida: Acari: Eriophyoidea) • *D.C.M. Manson*
ISBN 0-477-06746-8 • 14 Nov 1984 • 128 pp. $29.95

6 **Hydraenidae** (Insecta: Coleoptera) • *R.G. Ordish*
ISBN 0-477-06747-6 • 12 Nov 1984 • 64 pp. $18.60

7 **Cryptostigmata** (Arachnida: Acari) – a concise review • *M. Luxton*
ISBN 0-477-06762-X • 8 Dec 1985 • 112 pp. $29.95

8 **Calliphoridae** (Insecta: Diptera) • *James P. Dear*
ISBN 0-477-06764-6 • 24 Feb 1986 • 88 pp. $18.60

9 **Protura** (Insecta) • *S.L. Tuxen*
ISBN 0-477-06765-4 • 24 Feb 1986 • 52 pp. $18.60

10 **Tubulifera** (Insecta: Thysanoptera) • *Laurence A. Mound & Annette K. Walker*
ISBN 0-477-06784-0 • 22 Sep 1986 • 144 pp. $34.65

11 **Pseudococcidae** (Insecta: Hemiptera) • *J.M. Cox*
ISBN 0-477-06791-3 • 7 Apr 1987 • 232 pp. $49.95

12 **Pompilidae** (Insecta: Hymenoptera) • *A.C. Harris*
ISBN 0-477-02501-3 • 13 Nov 1987 • 160 pp. $39.95

13 **Encyrtidae** (Insecta: Hymenoptera) • *J.S. Noyes*
ISBN 0-477-02517-X • 9 May 1988 • 192 pp. $44.95

14 **Lepidoptera** – annotated catalogue, and keys to family-group taxa
J. S. Dugdale • ISBN 0-477-02518-8 • 23 Sep 1988 • 264 pp. $49.95

15 **Ambositrinae** (Insecta: Hymenoptera: Diapriidae) • *I.D. Naumann*
ISBN 0-477-02535-8 • 30 Dec 1988 • 168 pp. $39.95

16 **Nepticulidae** (Insecta: Lepidoptera) • *Hans Donner & Christopher Wilkinson*
ISBN 0-477-02538-2 • 28 Apr 1989 • 92 pp. $22.95

17 **Mymaridae** (Insecta: Hymenoptera) • *J.S. Noyes & E.W. Valentine*
ISBN 0-477-02542-0 • 28 Apr 1989 • 100 pp. $24.95

18 **Chalcidoidea** (Insecta: Hymenoptera) – introduction, and review of smaller families
J.S. Noyes & E.W. Valentine • ISBN 0-477-02545-5 • 2 Aug 1989 • 96 pp. $24.95

19 **Mantodea** (Insecta), with a review of aspects of functional morphology

19 **Mantodea** (Insecta), with a review of aspects of functional morphology
and biology • *G.W. Ramsay* • ISBN 0-477-02581-1 • 13 Jun 1990 • 96 pp. $24.95

20 **Bibionidae** (Insecta: Diptera) • *Roy A. Harrison*
ISBN 0-477-02595-1 • 13 Nov 1990 • 28 pp. $14.95

21 **Margarodidae** (Insecta: Hemiptera) • *C.F. Morales*
ISBN 0-477-02607-9 • 27 May 1991 • 124 pp. $34.95

22 **Notonemouridae** (Insecta: Plecoptera) • *I.D. McLellan*
ISBN 0-477-02518-8 • 27 May 1991 • 64 pp. $24.95

23 **Sciapodinae, Medeterinae** (Insecta: Diptera) with a generic review of the
Dolichopodidae • *D.J. Bickel* • ISBN 0-477-02627-3 • 13 Jan 1992 • 74 pp. .. $27.95

24 **Therevidae** (Insecta: Diptera) • *L. Lyneborg*
ISBN 0-477-02632-X • 4 Mar 1992 • 140 pp. $34.95

25 **Cercopidae** (Insecta: Homoptera) • *K.G.A. Hamilton & C.F. Morales*
ISBN 0-477-02636-2 • 25 May 1992 • 40 pp. $17.95

26 **Tenebrionidae** (Insecta: Coleoptera): catalogue of types and keys to taxa
J.C. Watt • ISBN 0-477-02639-7 • Jul1992 • 70 pp. $27.95

27 **Antarctoperlinae** (Insecta: Plecoptera) • *I.D. McLellan*
ISBN 0-477-01644-8 • 18 Feb 1993 • 70 pp. $27.95

28 **Larvae of Curculionoidea** (Insecta: Coleoptera): a systematic overview
Brenda M. May • ISBN 0-478-04505-0 • 14 Jun 1993 • 226 pp. $55.00

29 **Cryptorhynchinae** (Insecta: Coleoptera: Curculionidae)
C.H.C. Lyal • ISBN 0-478-04518-2 • 2 Dec 1993 • 308 pp. $65.00

30 **Hepialidae** (Insecta: Lepidoptera) • *J.S. Dugdale*
ISBN 0-478-04524-7 • 1 Mar 1994 • 164 pp. $42.50

31 **Talitridae** (Crustacea: Amphipoda) • *K.W. Duncan*
ISBN 0-478-04533-6 • 7 Oct 1994 • 128 pp. $36.00

32 **Sphecidae** (Insecta: Hymenoptera) • *A.C. Harris*
ISBN 0-478-04534-4 • 7 Oct 1994 • 112 pp. $33.50

33 **Moranilini** (Insecta: Hymenoptera) • *J.A. Berry*
ISBN 0-478-04538-7 • Apr 1995 • 82 pp. .... P.O.A.

NOTICES

This series of refereed occasional publications has been established to encourage those with expert knowledge to publish concise yet comprehensive accounts of elements in the New Zealand fauna. The series is professional in its conception and presentation, yet every effort is made to provide resources for identification and information that are accessible to the non-specialist.

'Fauna of N.Z.' deals with non-marine invertebrates only, since the vertebrates are well documented, and marine forms are covered by the series 'Marine Fauna of N.Z.'.

Contributions are invited from any person with the requisite specialist skills and resources. Material from the N.Z. Arthropod Collection is available for study.

Contributors should discuss their intentions with an appropriate member of the 'Fauna' Advisory Group or with the Series Editor before commencing work; all necessary guidance will be given.

Subscribers should address inquiries to 'Fauna of N.Z.', Library, Mt Albert Research Centre, Private Bag 92-169, Auckland, New Zealand.

Subscription categories: 'A' – standing orders; an invoice will be sent with each new issue, as soon after publication as possible. 'B' – promotional fliers with order forms will be sent from time to time.

Retail prices (see 'Titles in print', page 80) include packaging and surface postage. Subscribers in New Zealand and Australia pay the indicated amount in $NZ; GST is included in the price. Other subscribers pay the listed price in $US, or equivalent.

Back issues of all numbers are available, and new subscribers wishing to obtain a full set or a selection may request a discount. Booksellers and subscription agents are offered a trade discount of 20%.

NGA PAANUI

Kua whakatuuria teenei raarangi pukapuka hei whakahauhau ki nga tohunga whai maatauranga kia whakaatu i nga mea e paa ana ki nga kararehe o Niu Tiireni. He aahua tohunga teenei raarangi pukapuka, engari, ko te hiahia kia maarama ai te tuhituhi, kia moohio ai te maria ki nga tohu o ia ngaarara, o ia ngaarara, aa, kia whakaari i te maatauranga e paa ana ki a ratou.

Ko eenei pukapuka 'Fauna of New Zealand' kaaore e paa ana ki nga kararehe, ki nga ika, ki nga maataitai raanei. E tino moohiotia ana nga kararehe. Kei roto i nga pukapuka e kiia ana 'Marine Fauna of New Zealand' nga tuhituhi e paa ana ki nga ika me nga maataitai.

Tuhituhinga. Ko te tono ki nga tohunga kia tukua mai aa koutou pukapuka. E waatea ana te kohikohinga kararehe e kiia ana ko te New Zealand Arthropod Collection hei maatakitaki maau.

Me whaakii oo koutou whakaaro ki te mema o te kaahui tohutohu o 'Fauna' e tika ana, ki te Etita raanei, i mua i te tiimatanga tuhituhi.

Nga kai-hoko pukapuka. Me tuhi ki te 'Fauna of N.Z.' kei te Library, Mt Albert Research Centre, Private Bag 92-169, Auckland, New Zealand.

E rua nga tuumomo kai-hoko: 'A' – Kai-hoko tuumau; ka tukua ia pukapuka, ia pukapuka, me te kaute, i muri tonu i te taanga o taua pukapuka. 'B' – ka tukua nga paanui anake, a toona waa, a toona waa.

Te utu (tirohia te whaarangi 80): Ko te koopakitanga me te pane kuini kei roto i te utu. Me utu koutou e noho ana Niu Tiireni me Aahitereiria ki nga taara o Niu Tiireni. Ko eetahi atu me utu te whakaritenga i nga taara Marikena.

E toe ana nga pukapuka o mua. Mehemea e hiahia ana koe ki te katoa o nga pukapuka, tonoa mai kia heke iho te utu. E rua pai heneti te heke iho o te utu ki nga toa hoko pukapuka.